D0991882

AN

INTRODUCTION

TO

MODERN

LOGIC

An Elementary Textbook of Symbolic Logic

WILLIAM H. HALBERSTADT
Assistant Professor of Philosophy
University of Nevada

HARPER & BROTHERS, PUBLISHERS, NEW YORK

AN INTRODUCTION TO MODERN LOGIC:
An Elementary Textbook of Symbolic Logic
Copyright © 1960 by William H. Halberstadt

Printed in the United States of America

All rights in this book are reserved.
No part of the book may be used or reproduced
in any manner whatsoever without written permission except in the case of brief quotations
embodied in critical articles and reviews. For information address Harper & Brothers, 49 East
33rd Street, New York 16, N. Y.

BC
135
. H28

Library of Congress catalog card number: 60–7009

To my mother and father

Alma College Library
Alma, Michigan

Contents

PREFACE   xi
CHAPTER ONE: The Nature of Logic   1

    §1. Characteristics of Logic   1
    §2. A Note on Deduction   8

CHAPTER TWO: Twelve Valid Argument Forms   15

    §3. Modus Ponens   15
    §4. Statements of the Form P ⊃ Q   22
    §5. Proofs for the Validity of Arguments   28
    §6. The Fallacy of Affirming the Consequent   36
    §7. Modus Tollens   38
    §8. The Fallacy of Denying the Antecedent   44
    §9. The Hypothetical Syllogism   46
    §10. The Disjunctive Syllogism and the Commutativity
        of Disjunction   49
    §11. Atomic and Molecular Statements   53
    §12. The Constructive Dilemma   59
    §13. Simplification, Conjunction, and the Commutativity
        of Conjunction   63
    §14. Abbreviated Proofs of Validity   67
    §15. The Principle of Double Negation   69
    §16. The Principle of Addition   74

CHAPTER THREE: Definitions 76

§17. *Definition of* P ∨ Q 76
§18. *Definition of* P ⊃ Q 81
§19. *The Biconditional* 85
§20. *The Exclusive Disjunction* 89

CHAPTER FOUR: Truth Tables and Their Implications 93

§21. *Truth Tables for Negation and Conjunction* 93
§22. *Truth Tables for Statements of the Forms,*
    P ∨ Q, P ⊃ Q, P ≡ Q, *and* P ⓥ Q 98
§23. *Abbreviated Truth Tables* 100
§24. *Proving Validity and Invalidity by Truth Tables* 102
§25. *The* Reductio ad Absurdum *Method of Proving*
    Validity and Invalidity 110
§26. *Proving Consistency and Inconsistency* 117
§27. *Logical Equivalence* 125
§28. *Using Logical Equivalences in Proofs of Validity* 133
§29. *The Principle of Substitution* 140
§30. *The Conditional Method of Proving Validity* 149
§31. *The Indirect Method of Proving Validity* 156

CHAPTER FIVE: Quantification 162

§32. *Predicate-Subject Notation and Universal*
    Quantification 162
§33. *Universal Instantiation* 172
§34. *Universal Generalization* 175
§35. *Existential Quantification* 179
§36. *Existential Instantiation and Existential*
    Generalization 182
§37. *Definition of* (∃α)S 187
§38. *The Application of Truth Tables to Arguments*
    Involving Quantification 194
§39. *Proving Quantified Arguments Valid by the*
    Conditional and Indirect Methods 198

CHAPTER SIX: Conclusion   203

   §40. Final Remarks   203
   §41. Summary of Logical Principles   205

APPENDIX: Aristotelian Logic   207
INDEX OF ABBREVIATIONS   217
INDEX OF SPECIAL SYMBOLS   218
INDEX OF TOPICS   219

Preface

Logic textbooks frequently contain a presentation of *symbolic* logic which is either superficial or needlessly complex. This text attempts to hit a mean between these extremes. The essentials of a system comparable to that of Whitehead and Russell (and using, for the most part, their basic notation) are presented, including a propositional calculus and a functional calculus of the first order. Throughout, the text strives to be self-explanatory. The system is elementary, yet (I hope) is presented with thoroughness and clarity. I have tried to provide the student with abundant opportunity to master each principle before consideration of the next ones by including more than six hundred exercises in the text. The student is thereby enabled to gain facility in the actual *practice* of logic. While formal correctness is never sacrificed, constant stress is placed on the practical utility of symbolic logic—thus virtually all the exercises are given in linguistic form, with arguments chosen from philosophy, science, and everyday life.

To all of my colleagues, teachers, friends, and students, who, in various ways, have given me encouragement and assistance in the completion of this work, I am sincerely grateful. Especial thanks are due to Mr. Gerald S. Silberman, Lecturer in Mathematics at the University of Nevada, who read the manuscript and made many invaluable suggestions; to Dr. Robert T. Roelofs, Chairman of the Department of Philosophy at the University of Nevada, for his continued enthusiasm and encouragement in the project; to Dr. Cynthia A. Schuster, Professor of Philosophy at Montana State University, for reading an early draft of the manuscript and making helpful suggestions for its improvement; to Dr. Edward W.

Hiler and Dr. Charles E. Monson, Jr., formerly of the Department of Philosophy at the University of Nevada, for their encouraging comments on an early draft of the work; to my teacher, Dr. Atwell R. Turquette, Professor of Philosophy at the University of Illinois, for much of my knowledge of symbolic logic; to Mr. William C. Stone, one of my former students, who assisted in typing the manuscript; and to my friend and former student, Mr. John C. Ivey, for his assistance in proofreading the manuscript.

WILLIAM H. HALBERSTADT

Reno, Nevada
January, 1960

AN INTRODUCTION TO MODERN LOGIC

CHAPTER ONE

The Nature of Logic

§1. Characteristics of Logic

What do people mean when they say "Now that sounds logical"? What is it that determines whether or not something is logical? Or, generally speaking, *what is logic?*

We can offer a brief definition of "logic" as *"the rules of correct reasoning"*. But this definition tells us no more than the word "logic" does at this stage, since we do not yet know what the "rules of correct reasoning" are. In a sense, this entire book will be an extended definition of "logic", or, to put it differently, an explication of the "rules of correct reasoning".

However, the important thing to be gained from this book is not a memorized definition of "logic", but rather a knowledge of some of the basic elements of logic and an understanding of how to apply them. For logic is a practical activity as well as a theoretical discipline.

Logic is an activity to be used outside, as well as within, the classroom. It is an activity to be used in everyday life, in business, in science. With the current state of uncertainty in international affairs, it is more important than ever that everyone be able to look with the uncompromising eye of logical analysis at all persuasive propaganda which is thrown his way. Decisions for action must be based on correct reasoning, not on emotional appeal.

Aristotle, the great logician of ancient Greece, wrote a book on rhetoric, which to him meant the art of persuasion. He realized the distinction between the two kinds of appeal to people's assent: the logical and the emotive. How often do people today listen to political speeches without an awareness of this distinction? Are you sure that it is the logic, and not the appeal to the emotions, which wins

1

your consent to political arguments? We must be ever cautious not to be moved by persuasion which is eloquent but illogical. The study of logic will make us keenly aware of this.

There is every sort of situation, be it profound or commonplace, in which logic is indispensable. The reasoning that the grocer gives as to why a can of fruit should be three cents more at his store than at the supermarket in the next block—does his argument hold water? Or what about the argument that you should be nice to Aunt Sarah so that she will bequeath you her millions—how logical is it?

Logic is not reserved for special situations; rather it is a special situation where logical thinking is not required. Businessmen have need of logic. What will be the consequence of the proposed salary raise, or of the proposed new building? Law would be lost without logic. Science relies heavily upon logic. Mathematics, according to Whitehead and Russell, can be reduced to logic.

The practical utility of logic will become evident as the study of this text progresses. Yet we must discover more about the nature of logic before we can fully appreciate its value to us.

We can learn something about logic by examining an example of reasoning which everyone will agree "sounds logical." Suppose two college students are concerned about whether a heavy rain will mean that the afternoon ball game will have to be canceled. Their conversation might run something like this:

"If it's raining heavily," says the first, "then the game will have to be canceled." The second, looking out the window and seeing the rain, replies, "It's raining heavily." The first then concludes, "So the game will have to be canceled."

Let us restate this conversation in the following manner:

EXAMPLE   1

> If it's raining heavily, then the game will have to be canceled.
> It's raining heavily.
> So the game will have to be canceled.

The first two statements of Example 1 are advanced to substantiate the third. A series of statements like this constitutes what logicians call an "argument". "Argument" is here used in a technical sense which has nothing to do with the common usage of the term to designate a disagreement. An argument to the logician is a series of statements such that at least one of them is advanced to substantiate another. Those which are intended to give such substantiation are called "premises". Since an argument may have one or several premises, it will be convenient to introduce the term "premise set" to designate a set of premises (i.e., more than one). Let us also introduce the term "conclusion" to designate the statement in an argument which is presented as following from the premise or premise set. In the argument of Example 1, which has more than one premise, the first two statements constitute the premise set; and the third statement is the conclusion, as the word "so" (which in this context is equivalent to "therefore") indicates.

We must be cautious about defining "premise" or "premise set" and "conclusion". We do not wish to say that in an argument the premise or premise set is that which *does in fact* substantiate the conclusion, nor do we wish to say that the conclusion of an argument is that which *does in fact* follow from the premise or premise set. The reason for our caution is that some arguments may be defective; and then the premise or premise set may *not* substantiate the conclusion, and the conclusion may *not* follow from the premise or premise set. Let us accordingly introduce the following definitions:

An argument is a series of statements such that at least one of them is advanced to substantiate another. (Here the phrase "is advanced to substantiate" makes clear that such substantiation, while always intended, is not always the case.)

The statement or statements in an argument which are intended to substantiate another statement in the argument we shall call the "premise" or "premise set" of that argument. (Again, note the word "intended".)

The conclusion of an argument is that statement which is said to follow from the premise or premise set. (Here the phrase "is said to" takes care of those cases in which the conclusion does not, in fact, follow from the premises.)

Schematically, an argument may be represented as follows:

EXAMPLE 2

Premise or premise set $\Big\{$ ——————————————
———————————————

Conclusion Therefore ———————————————

(The blank lines indicate English statements.)

Tentatively, we said that logic is "the rules of correct reasoning." In light of our discovery that there are correct and incorrect arguments, we can now further specify that logic is the "rules of correct reasoning" in getting from the premise or premise set of an argument to its conclusion. This process of "getting from" the premise or premise set of an argument to its conclusion is usually called "inference". We must yet distinguish correct from incorrect ways of inferring. But it will be convenient first to note various ways in which arguments, both correct and incorrect, may appear in English, so that we may know when we are dealing with an argument and when we are dealing with merely a series of statements, none of which is intended to support another.

Frequently, we encounter arguments in everyday life which are not so neatly stated as that in Example 1. Sometimes, for instance, the conclusion is given first, and the supporting premise or premise set is given last, as in the following example:

EXAMPLE 3

I'll get good grades in school this year; because if I do well I'll get good grades, and I will do well.

Restated in standard form this argument appears as follows:

EXAMPLE 4

Premise set $\begin{cases} \text{If I do well, then I'll get good grades.} \\ \text{I will do well.} \end{cases}$

Conclusion   Therefore I'll get good grades.

Example 4 is equivalent to Example 3, the only difference being that, in Example 4, the statements are rearranged so that the premises come first, and the conclusion last. Also, in Example 4 the conclusion is indicated by the word "therefore", which did not appear in the original. In Example 3, however, it is evident what the conclusion is since the supporting premises are preceded by the word "because".

Thus there are different means of indicating a conclusion in English. The most usual are to precede it with some expression such as "therefore", "so", "thus", "hence", "accordingly", "consequently", or "it follows that". Or, if the conclusion is stated first, one usually indicates that it is the conclusion by following it with a word like "because", "for", or "since"; and then giving the supporting premise or premise set, as was done in Example 3.

Sometimes, even in what we have called "correct" arguments, the conclusion is merely *probable* even though the premises are known to be true. In the arguments we have thus far considered this was not the case; for if the premises of these arguments are true, then the conclusions are true. But what about the following example?

EXAMPLE 5

Crow a is black.
Crow b is black.
Crow c is black.

.

.

.

[etc.]

.

.

Crow n is black.
Hence all crows are black.

In Example 5 the conclusion is not *necessarily* true, even though the premises are true. The reason for this is fairly obvious, namely, one cannot observe all crows to draw the infallible conclusion that all crows are black. One can only observe what one hopes is a fairly representative sample; and then attach a degree of *probability* to his conclusion, thus allowing for the possibility of that albino crow that was not observed. Or he may even incorporate the statement of probability into his conclusion, in this manner: "Hence *it is probable* that all crows are black."

The distinction between arguments whose conclusions are presented as following necessarily from the premises (as in Examples 1 and 4) and those whose conclusions are presented as probable even though their premises are true (as in Example 5) supplies us with a basis for distinguishing two different types of logic. These two types are known, respectively, as *"deductive logic"* (or simply, *"deduction"*) and *"inductive logic"* (or *"induction"*).

We can ascertain whether an argument is *deductive* or *inductive* by ascertaining whether the conclusion is presented as following *necessarily* or *probably* from the premise or premise set. If the conclusion is presented as following necessarily from the premise or premise set, then the argument is deductive; whereas if the conclusion is presented as following only probably from the premise or premise set, even though the statement of probability be incorporated into the conclusion, then the argument is inductive.

Note that we have made the distinction between deductive and inductive arguments in terms of whether the conclusion is *presented as following* necessarily or probably from the premises. We have again been careful not to say that the conclusion of an argument does, in fact, so follow from its premises, since some arguments may be defective.

A further distinction, not especially peculiar to logic, but rather to English grammar and usage as well, will be here made so that confusion will not arise in the following pages. It is the distinction which logicians customarily make between the *use* and the *mention* of a symbol. Let us consider the symbol "logic". This is a symbol, more normally called a "word", consisting of five smaller symbols, "l", "o", "g", "i", "c". When I *mention* the symbol, I am talking about it merely as a symbol, and not as the name of any study. Further, I *mention* the symbol by putting it within quotation marks. However, when I *use* the symbol, I am not talking about it, but rather using it as I would any other word, namely to form a sentence. Consider the following two statements:

S₁. "Logic" has five letters.
S₂. Logic is a study indispensable to all aspects of human living.

In S₁, the symbol "Logic" is *mentioned* (in quotation marks). In S₂, however, there are no quotation marks because the symbol in question is *used* as a word serving a grammatical function in the sentence. The distinction between the *use* and the *mention* of a symbol will serve to eliminate ambiguities.

Exercises

group A

1. What do logicians mean by the term "argument"?
2. What is a premise?

3. What is a conclusion?
4. What is meant by the term "inference"?
5. In your own words, state the distinction between induction and deduction.
6. How are conclusions usually indicated in English?
7. Construct five deductive arguments, and be prepared to explain why they are deductive rather than inductive.
8. Construct five inductive arguments, and be prepared to explain why they are not deductive.
9. Construct five series of statements which constitute neither deductive nor inductive arguments, and be prepared to state why they are not arguments.
10. Distinguish between the use and the mention of a symbol.

GROUP B

Punctuate the following English sentences correctly.

11. Dogs bark
12. Dogs bark is true
13. Dogs bark is an English sentence
14. Dogs have four feet
15. Dog has three letters

GROUP C

For each of the following series of statements, ascertain whether or not it is an argument. If it is an argument, state whether it is deductive or inductive, and why; then write the argument in standard form, indicating premise (or premise set) and conclusion.

Sample exercise:
    Socrates is mortal; because all men are mortal, and Socrates is a man.
    Answer: This is a deductive argument, because the conclusion is presented as following necessarily from the premise set.
    The argument may be formalized as follows:

Premise set $\left\{ \begin{array}{l} \text{All men are mortal.} \\ \\ \text{Socrates is a man.} \end{array} \right.$

Conclusion   Therefore Socrates is mortal.

Do each of the following exercises in the same manner:

16. Jones committed the murder, because I heard him threaten to do it.
17. People may be divided into two classifications: those who are wide awake in the morning, and those who can't really get going until about noon. Those of the former type are usually a terrible bore; it's the others who are usually interesting.

18. All crows are black. This is a crow. Therefore this is black.

19. All crows are red. This is a crow. Therefore this is red.

20. All glubs are blorid. This is a glub. Therefore this is blorid.

21. I like to drink gin and tonic, but it always makes me ill when I drink a lot of it. It must be the tonic that does it: I'll have to drink straight gin in the future.

22. I like to drink gin and tonic, but it always makes me ill when I drink a lot of it. I suppose the safest bet would be to avoid alcohol altogether.

23. Plato, who studied with Socrates, held that there was an intelligible World of Ideas or archetypes, of which things in the world of appearance were mere copies, or imitations. Some scholars have maintained that Plato derived this doctrine from Socrates. At any rate, Aristotle, who in turn studied with Plato, rejected the Doctrine of Ideas.

24. If it's clear tomorrow, Grace will go shopping; but if it rains, she'll stay home. It's a sure bet that it will either be clear or rain tomorrow, so we can safely say that Grace will either go shopping or stay home.

25. All dogs are furry animals. Some dogs have short tails. Therefore some short-tailed animals are furry.

26. Grace and Arthur are bound to go to the dance together. They've gone to every social function together as long as I can remember.

27. Grace is going to go to the dance; because Arthur's going to ask her, and if Arthur asks her, she'll go.

28. Bentham and Mill both proposed that that which was ultimately desirable was the greatest good for the greatest number. However, Bentham made no distinction between qualitatively different pleasures and pains. Mill tried to remedy this in his theory of utilitarianism.

29. If the moon is made of green cheese, then it goes well on crackers. The moon is made of green cheese. Therefore it goes well on crackers.

30. If the moon is made of green cheese, I'll eat my hat. If I eat my hat, I'll get indigestion. If I get indigestion, I won't want to eat any green cheese anyhow.

§2.   A Note on Deduction

A good way to begin the study of logic is to learn something about deduction, since it provides, better than does induction, an appreciation of the value of logical form. The "rules of correct reasoning" for deductive logic can give more precise formulae for ascertaining correct arguments than can those of induction because of the very nature of the two types of logic. In correct arguments of deductive logic, we know that if the premises are true, the conclusion will necessarily follow. Thus there is never any question as to the certitude of the conclusion of a correct deductive argument which has true premises. But in inductive logic, as we have seen, true premises do not necessarily imply a true conclusion. A knowledge of some elementary principles of deductive logic will enable anyone to ascertain the correctness of a great many arguments encountered in everyday life, by providing him with some easily formalized "rules of correct reasoning". It will be a system of deductive logic which we shall present in this book.

But before we begin a presentation of the elements of *deductive* logic, let us find out something about the nature of deductive systems in general. This we shall do by looking for a moment at an age-old deductive system familiar to most of us, namely Euclidean geometry. Although Euclid himself made some major mistakes in constructing his geometry, we shall consider Euclidean geometry as corrected by later geometers, in order to understand the nature of a deductive system. Euclidean geometry, like any deductive system, involves a codification of principles by which conclusions that are consistent with the initial assumptions of the system can be inferred. Yet, and this is a significant fact overlooked by many students of geometry, *other systems of geometry are possible;* i.e., other initial assumptions may be adopted which lead to conclusions quite different from those of Euclidean geometry. If one accepts the basic assumptions of the Euclidean system, then its conclusions may be drawn with infallible necessity. But one need not accept the assumptions of Euclidean geometry; one may accept an alternative system, having different assumptions, which might contradict Euclidean geometry. In fact, it is just such an alternative geometry that is required by Einstein's famed theory of relativity. Each geometry is self-consistent; that is to say that, if one accepts its basic assumptions, any conclusions drawn from these assumptions will not contradict one another. Thus, in Euclidean geometry, one cannot conclude that two given right triangles both are and are not congruent. Yet different systems, while themselves *internally* consistent, may be mutually contradictory; since, inasmuch as they start from different assumptions, the conclusions of one system may well differ from those of another system.

The same is true of deductive systems of logic. When we speak of the conclusion of a correct deductive argument *necessarily* following from the premises, of what sort of necessity, then, do we speak? We can mean necessity only *within* the system. There is no *absolute* necessity, inasmuch as alternative systems are possible. Thus, a conclusion which follows of necessity from the premises of an argument in one system of deductive logic may be quite inadmissible in another system of deductive logic, even if one were given the same premises.

How then, does one choose between equally legitimate, though mutually contradictory, systems of deductive logic? Unfortunately, the choice cannot, strictly speaking, be a logical one, but must be *extralogical,* i.e., it must be made *outside* the systems of logic being considered. One of the criteria for the choice of systems seems to be more a *psychological* than a *logical* one. Thus the logic we here present is universally accepted by common sense, i.e., it is psychologically agreeable to us. Further, *utility* is probably another criterion in the selection of systems. For all practical purposes, the system of deductive logic presented in this book is the most useful. It is only more advanced problems in the theoretical sciences that require different systems of logic.

Let us illustrate by citing just one of the things which our logic assumes. It assumes that any meaningful statement is either true or false, that there is no third possibility. This assumption is psychologically acceptable, and useful as well. Nevertheless scientists have found uses for systems of logic which assume that a meaningful statement can have more values than the traditional *true* and *false*.

Perhaps a question occurs to the reader at this point, namely: If the choice of logical systems is not determined by any necessity, and if I am to be guided in my decisions by logic and not emotion, how is this possible? This is not nearly so paradoxical as it sounds at first. Just because there is no ultimate necessity determining the choice of logical systems, this does not mean that logic is completely irrational or based on the merest whim. We can still codify a set of *consistent* principles to which we are ready to give assent.

It may also occur to the reader that the phrase "principles of correct reasoning" is somewhat misleading. And indeed it is, for what may be correct in one system may be quite incorrect in another system. We shall, in the course of this book, discover what are the "correct principles" with regard to the standard system of deductive logic that we shall study. Nevertheless, with regard to *any* deductive system, when we ask whether an argument is *correct,* we can mean one of two things. First of all, we might mean, does the conclusion really follow from the premise or premise set? Or, in other words, does the premise or premise set *imply* the conclusion? Consider the following argument:

EXAMPLE   6

> If I have enough money, I shall go to the movies tonight. I have enough money.
>
> Therefore I shall go to the movies tonight.

In this first sense of *correctness,* we could say that the argument is correct; because the premise set really does imply the conclusion. The conclusion is not only *presented as* following necessarily from the premise set of this argument, but further it *does in fact* follow necessarily from it. Let us say that such an argument is a *valid* deductive argument. We shall thus abandon the ambiguous term "correct" and use the term "valid" to cover its first sense. An *"invalid* deductive argument" may then be defined as "one in which, though the conclusion is *presented as* following necessarily from the premises, it does *not* in fact so follow".

But what about the second sense of "correct"? Consider again the argument of Example 6. Suppose that the first premise is true, namely that if I do in fact have enough money, then I shall go to the movies tonight. But suppose that the second premise is *false;* suppose that in fact I do *not* have enough money. Then the conclusion, that I shall go to the movies tonight, may *not* be true (unless some kind friend donates the admission fee; in which case the conclusion of the argument would be true not by virtue of the truth of the premises, but rather by virtue of the philanthropic tendencies of my benefactor). The argument of Example 6 would then be incorrect in the second sense of correctness. Let us again abandon the term "correct" and use the term "sound" to cover this second sense. Then we shall say of the argument of Example 6 that, although it is a *valid* deductive argument, it is *unsound* if not all of its premises are true. All that is required for a deductive argument to be valid is that the premise or premise set, *whether true or false,* imply the conclusion. A sound deductive argument is a valid one that *does* have true premises, and so, of course, its conclusion will be true. Let us summarize this distinction by means of the following definitions:

A valid deductive argument is one whose premise or premise set implies the conclusion. (In other words, a valid deductive argument is one whose conclusion follows necessarily from its premise or premise set. The premise or premise set may be true or false; if true, then the conclusion will be true.)

A sound deductive argument is a valid argument with true premises.

Note that not just any argument with true premises is sound; a sound deductive argument must first of all be *valid,* and secondly, it must have true premises. Thus, the following argument, which has true premises, is unsound, because it is not valid.

EXAMPLE 7

> The moon is a satellite of the earth.
> The earth is not a flat disc.
> Hence the moon is made of green cheese.

This argument cannot be valid because the conclusion cannot possibly be drawn from the premises. And since it is not valid, it cannot be sound.

We have defined the terms "valid" and "sound". Let us now make sure we know the meaning of "invalid" and of "unsound". We already said that an invalid argument is one in which, though the conclusion is presented as following necessarily from the premises, it does not in fact so follow. An invalid argument, in other words, displays no necessary connection between the premises and the conclusion, as in Example 8:

EXAMPLE 8

> All crows are black.
> Therefore the moon is made of red cheese.

What are and are not the "necessary connections" between premise or premise set and conclusion which make a deductive argument valid will depend on the "rules of correct reasoning" which shall be presented in this book.

It remains for us yet to define "unsound". An unsound argument in deductive logic is either a valid argument with at least one false premise, or an invalid argument. Thus the category of unsoundness overlaps that of invalidity. This we can represent schematically as follows:

EXAMPLE 9

Deductive Arguments

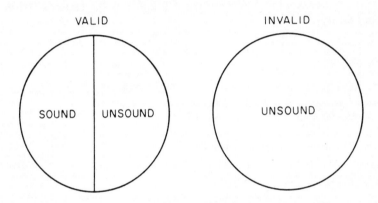

Sometimes logic is accused, by those who do not understand its principles, of proving all manner of absurd things, such as that the moon is made of green cheese.

EXAMPLE 10

If Socrates was a philosopher, then the moon is made of green cheese.
Socrates was a philosopher.
Therefore the moon is made of green cheese.

Certainly, in Example 10, logic has in no sense of the word "proved" that the moon is made of green cheese. It has only shown that *if* the premises of this argument are accepted, then the conclusion will follow of necessity. Example 10 illustrates the same valid argument form as do Examples 1, 4, and 6. But, and this is the important point, the validity of the argument form in no way vouches for the truth of any of the statements which we insert into the form. The valid *forms* of deductive arguments are no guarantee of the *soundness* of particular arguments having these forms. Thus, in Example 10, although the form of the argument is valid, one of the premises is false, and hence the argument is unsound. Once the valid argument forms are known, it is of course necessary to know whether the particular statements used in any instance are true or false in order to ascertain whether or not the argument is sound.

But since a deductive argument must first be valid before it can be sound, let us first establish some valid argument forms or "rules of correct reasoning," and reserve till later our discussion of truth and falsity.

EXERCISES

31. What is the ultimate ground of justification of any deductive system?
32. What is a valid deductive argument?
33. What is a sound deductive argument?
34. What is an invalid deductive argument?
35. What is an unsound deductive argument?

CHAPTER TWO

Twelve Valid Argument Forms

§3. Modus Ponens

A good starting point for our discussion of valid argument forms is the form exhibited by the arguments of Examples 1, 4, 6, and 10. This we shall call "Valid Argument Form No. 1", or simply "A_1". It is the following principle, known as *"modus ponens"*:

> If *P,* then *Q*
> *P*
> Therefore *Q*

Note that we are using *statement variables* ($P, Q, R, \cdots$)[1] to represent statements. Since "if $\cdots$ then —" is a frequently encountered expression, the symbol $\supset$ is used as a kind of short-hand designation for it. It is called a "horseshoe". The expression $P \supset Q$ may be read, "If *P,* then *Q.*" Further, since "therefore" often occurs, we may designate a conclusion by $\therefore$ rather than by the word "therefore". The symbol $\therefore$ will also designate the equivalents of "therefore", such as "hence", "thus", "accordingly", "consequently", etc.

In symbolic notation, then, the argument form, A_1, may be written as follows:

> A_1: $P \supset Q$
> P
> $\therefore Q$

---

[1] Strictly, this should be written: ("*P*", "*Q*", "*R*", $\cdots$), because we are *mentioning* rather than *using* the symbols. However, we adopt the convention of not using quotation marks with symbols which are not words of the English language but are rather part of the vocabulary of symbolic logic (e.g., the letters *P, Q,* etc., as well as other special symbols like $\supset$ and $\therefore$), when it is clear from the context that they are *mentioned* rather than *used*.

This is the general statement of A_1. Any specific argument which is of the form A_1 will be said to be an *"instance"* of A_1. Thus, for example, while the arguments of Examples 1, 4, 6, and 10 are all different arguments in regard to their *content,* they are nevertheless all instances of the same *form,* namely, A_1. If we recognize this, we shall see at once an advantage of logic: instead of looking for a different logical analysis each time a new argument is encountered, we will be able to test for validity with the aid of a small number of principles such as A_1, so long as we approach any argument from the point of view of its *form* rather than its *content.*

In order to abstract the *form* of an argument, it will be useful to translate it into a completely symbolic language, so that we will not be confused with the *content.* A mere consideration of content would be hopeless in ascertaining the validity of a long argument. Usually, however, such arguments can be handled quite easily if one looks to their form only.

Let us try putting an actual English argument that is an instance of A_1 into completely symbolic form. The statement variables (P and Q) in A_1 will be replaced with letters chosen to designate English statements of our argument. These letters will regularly be the initial letter (or letters) of an important word (or words) in the English statements for which they stand. We shall see how this is done by considering the instance of A_1 stated below:

EXAMPLE 11

> If Jane has a fever, then Jane is ill.
> Jane has a fever.
> Therefore Jane is ill.

The first premise of this argument is actually a compound statement consisting of two smaller statements joined by the phrase "if ··· then —", which will be translated by the horseshoe ($\supset$). The smallest statement-units shall be called *"atomic* statements", and any compound statement shall be called a *"molecular* statement". Thus, the first premise of Example 11 is a molecular statement consisting of two atomic statements joined by the horseshoe. These atomic statements are:

1. Jane has a fever.
2. Jane is ill.

These two atomic statements are, in fact, the only ones used in Example 11. In the argument, the first of these will be taken as an instance of P in A_1, and the second as an instance of Q. The first may be symbolized by JF, which is a combination of the initial letters of the subject of the sentence ("Jane") and the most important word of the predicate ("fever"). Likewise, "Jane is ill" may be symbolized by JI.

Thus the completely symbolic translation of our argument will be as follows:

EXAMPLE 12

    JF ⊃ JI
    JF
    ∴ JI

Sometimes one letter, rather than two, will suffice to symbolize an English statement. Thus R alone could well represent "It is raining." Convenience will determine whether one or two letters will be used to symbolize any given English statement.

One further thing should be noted about Example 12. JF is *uniformly* taken as an instance of P in A_1, and JI *uniformly* as an instance of Q. Thus:

JF	⊃	JI
P	⊃	Q

∴	JI
∴	Q

The following, accordingly, is not a legitimate instance of A_1:

EXAMPLE 13

> If Jane has a fever, then Jane is ill.
> This crow is black.
> Therefore Socrates is mortal.

In order to symbolize this argument, we shall use the following notation:

JF will represent the atomic statement "Jane has a fever."
JI will represent the atomic statement "Jane is ill."
CB will represent the atomic statement "This crow is black."
SM will represent the atomic statement "Socrates is mortal."

Now let us try to fit this argument into the form A_1, and see what happens:

JF	⊃	JI
P	⊃	Q

CB
P

∴	SM
∴	Q

The result violates our demand for *uniform replacement* for the variables P and Q. P is first replaced by JF, and then again by CB. Also, Q is first replaced by JI, and then later by SM.

Let us note a few conventions which shall be followed throughout this text. When we present an argument which is to be put into symbolic form, there will be written, in parentheses at the end of the argument, the suggested notation. This notation will consist of appropriate letters representing the atomic statements in the argument. Further, the letters which designate the various atomic statements in the argument will be presented *in the same order* as the order in which these atomic statements first appear in the English formulation of the argument, thus:

EXAMPLE 14

If Jane has a fever, then Jane is ill.
Jane has a fever.
Therefore Jane is ill.   (JF, JI)

Here JF, since it appears first within the parentheses, represents the first atomic statement which appears in the English statement of the argument, namely, "Jane has a fever"; and JI, since it appears second, represents the second atomic statement to appear in English, namely, "Jane is ill."

Thus far we have said that A_1 is valid without justifying its validity. Since no ultimate justification is possible for any logical system, we cannot give one for this fundamental principle of our system, and must introduce it as an assumption. Yet A_1 is one of the principles in our logic to which we said common sense gives its assent. We shall try to illustrate it, therefore, on commonsense grounds. Referring to Example 14, let us see what is involved in A_1. If we know that the first premise is true, namely, that *if* Jane has a fever, then she is ill; and if we further know that the second premise is true, namely that Jane does in fact have a fever, then common sense must conclude that Jane is ill. The "if"s in the preceding statement indicate that we do not know that the argument is *sound,* but that we do give assent to its validity. All that Example 14 states is that *if* the premises are true, whether they are in fact or not, then the conclusion follows of necessity. Symbolically, if JF $\supset$ JI is given (which it is, in the first premise of Example 14), and if JF is further given (as it is in the second premise of Example 14), then we may conclude JI (as is done in the conclusion of Example 14). The reader is encouraged to construct other instances of A_1 to help convince him of its validity.

EXERCISES

GROUP A

36. What is the technical name for A_1?
37. What is meant by the term "statement variable"?
38. What is meant by an *"instance"* of a valid argument form?

GROUP B

For each of the following arguments:

a. Translate into symbolic form.
b. Show the replacements for P and Q in the form A_1 by means of a diagram like the following:

c. On the basis of the diagram, state whether the argument is or is not a legitimate instance of A_1.

> *Sample exercise:*
>   If lead is soft, then it may be easily bent.
>   Lead is soft.
>   Therefore it may be easily bent.   (LS, EB)
>
> *Answer:*
>   *Part a*   LS ⊃ EB
>   LS
>   ∴ EB

Part b

LS	⊃	EB
P	⊃	Q

LS
P

∴	EB
∴	Q

Part c   This argument is a legitimate instance of A_1.

Do the following exercises in the same manner:

39. If Arthur saves his money, then he will be able to take Grace to the movies this weekend.
    Arthur saves his money.
    Therefore he will be able to take Grace to the movies this weekend.
       (SM, TG)

40. If Arthur is frugal, then he will save his money.
    Arthur will save his money.
    Therefore Arthur is frugal.   (AF, SM)

41. If Arthur is frugal, then he will save his money.
    Arthur is frugal.
    Therefore he will be able to take Grace to the movies this weekend.   (AF, SM, TG)

42. If Arthur wants to take Grace to the movies, then he will have to save his money.
    Arthur wants to take Grace to the movies.
    Therefore he will have to save his money.   (TG, SM)

43. If Arthur is going to take Grace to the movies, then he is planning to take her to coffee afterwards.
    Arthur is planning to take her to coffee afterwards.
    Therefore Arthur is a gentleman.   (TG, C, AG)

44. If Arthur is going to take Grace to the movies, then Grace will undoubtedly tell Jane.

Arthur is going to take Grace to the movies.
Therefore Grace will undoubtedly tell Jane.   (AG, GJ)

45. If Grace tells Jane, then Jane is going to be jealous.
Jane is going to be jealous.
Therefore Jane will try to get John to take her to the movies.   (GJ, JJ, M)

46. If John prefers a quiet evening at home, then Jane will be disappointed.
John prefers a quiet evening at home.
Therefore Jane will be disappointed.   (QE, JD)

47. If Jane is disappointed, then she will be even more furious at Arthur.
Jane is disappointed.
Therefore she will be even more furious at Arthur.   (JD, FA)

48. If Arthur goes bowling with John tonight, he will be broke this weekend.
Arthur has invited Grace to the movies.
Therefore Grace will be disappointed.   (BT, BW, IG, GD)

49. If Grace is disappointed, Jane will be delighted.
Jane will be delighted.
Therefore Grace is disappointed.   (GD, JD)

50. If the movie is enjoyable, Grace will be glad that she went.
Grace will be glad that she went.
Therefore the movie is enjoyable.   (ME, GG)

§4. Statements of the Form $P \supset Q$

Thus far, when we have been considering statements of the form $P \supset Q$, we have encountered statements in the English language which contained the words "if" and "then", and which had the "if" clause stated first. A typical example is this:

EXAMPLE 15

If the sun goes around the earth, then Venus goes around the earth.

If the suggested symbolic translation for the atomic statements are SE and VE, respectively, the statement would be translated into symbolic form as follows: SE $\supset$ VE.

Not all English statements of the form $P \supset Q$ are as neatly stated as that in Example 15. One of the commonest variants results from the omission of the word "then." Thus one could simply say: "If the sun goes around the earth, Venus goes around the earth." This would still be translated by SE $\supset$ VE.

Another common variant results from reversing the order of the "if" and "then" clauses, and omitting the word "then," as in the following example: "I would like Jones better if he would be more dependable." If the suggested translations of the atomic statements are LJ and MD, respectively, then the statement would be translated MD ⊃ LJ and not LJ ⊃ MD, because the statement means: "If Jones would be more dependable, then I would like him better", to put it into standard form.

Sometimes, instead of the word "then", one will find the phrase "this means", or "this means that", as in the following statement: "If the boss fires me, this means [or: this means that] I will be out of a job." Using the notation BF, OJ, the statement would be translated BF ⊃ OJ.

The "then" clause is sometimes introduced by the word "implies." Thus, "The acceptance of Euclidean geometry implies the acceptance of a three-dimensional space" means "If Euclidean geometry is accepted, then one must accept a three-dimensional space." Using EG, TD, this is translated EG ⊃ TD.

The subjunctive form "had such-and-such occurred" indicates an "if" clause. Thus, "Had it rained, the pavement would be wet", and "The pavement would be wet had it rained", both mean "If it had rained, then the pavement would be wet", and may be translated R ⊃ PW.

Likewise, the word "whenever" indicates an "if" clause. Thus, "Whenever Marie flies into a rage, this means one should be careful!" is equivalent to "If Marie flies into a rage, then one should be careful." "One should be careful whenever Marie flies into a rage" also means the same thing. These statements may be translated MF ⊃ C.

The various types of English statements thus far presented that are instances of the form $P \supset Q$ should present no trouble. The ones which follow may present some difficulty at first, however, and should be thoroughly mastered before the reader proceeds to the exercises. These new forms involve a consideration of necessary and sufficient conditions, and the phrase "only if".

Using the symbolic statement W ⊃ M, which shall stand for "If this is a whale, then it is a mammal", let us illustrate what is meant by necessary and sufficient conditions. If the animal about which we are talking is in fact a whale, then it necessarily is a mammal. Hence mammality is a necessary condition for something to be a whale. If the animal were not a mammal, i.e., if the necessary condition of our statement were not true, then the animal could not be a whale, for all whales are mammals. In other words, it is a whale *only if* it is a mammal.

Note that "only if", in this last statement, is not equivalent to "if", but rather to "then". "This is a whale only if it is a mammal", in other words, means that this is a whale only under the condition that it is a mammal, or that a necessary condition for it to be a whale is that it be a mammal. We reiterate, if the animal were not a mammal, i.e., if the necessary condition were not true, then the animal could not be a whale. Thus, "This is a whale only if it is a mammal" means "If this is a whale, then it is a mammal", and may be translated $W \supset M$.

From the above considerations, it may be observed that, in $W \supset M$, M is a necessary condition for W. To state it differently, the necessary condition of a hypothetical conditional (i.e., of a statement of the form $P \supset Q$) is its right-hand member.

But what about *sufficient* conditions? Consider the following statements:

   a. If this is a whale, then it is a mammal.
   b. If this is a cat, then it is a mammal.
   c. If this is a dog, then it is a mammal.
   d. If this is a rabbit, then it is a mammal.

Being a whale is a sufficient condition for something to be a mammal. If it is a whale, then it is a mammal, as statement *a* says. Being a cat is also a sufficient condition for something to be a mammal. Yet it is not *necessary* for something to be whale for it to be a mammal; it is only *sufficient* for something to be a whale for it to be a mammal. For other things besides whales are also mammals, such as cats and dogs and rabbits, as statements *b* through *d* indicate.

Under the condition that something is a whale, it will be a mammal. But this is not the only condition under which it could be a mammal; it could also be a mammal if it were a cat or a dog or a rabbit. Hence, being a whale is a sufficient, but not a necessary, condition for something to be a mammal.

Thus, in the statement W ⊃ M, W is a sufficient condition for M; i.e., the sufficient condition of a hypothetical conditional is its left-hand member.

Some students find it useful to remember that the sufficient condition is the left-hand member of a hypothetical conditional and the necessary condition the right-hand member by means of the following device: S ⊃ N, which is simply the word "sun" with the "u" on its side. The "S", of course, stands for "sufficient condition", and the "N" represents "necessary condition". A device like this, however handy it may be, must not replace understanding of the principles involved.

We have so far been referring to the *left-hand member* or the *right-hand member* of a hypothetical conditional statement. This is, of course, an accurate description, but we should be aware that there are technical names for these left- and right-hand members. The left-hand member of the hypothetical conditional statement is called the "antecedent"; the right-hand member is called the "consequent". Using this more appropriate terminology, we may recapitulate what has been said about necessary and sufficient conditions, and about the phrase "only if", in the following three statements:

1. *The necessary condition of a hypothetical conditional statement, i.e., the consequent, is a statement which must be true if that which is said to imply it, i.e., the antecedent, is true.*

2. *The sufficient condition of a hypothetical conditional statement, i.e., the antecedent, is a statement whose truth is a possible condition under which the statement it is said to imply, i.e., the consequent, is true.*

3. *When, in a hypothetical conditional statement, the antecedent is said to be true "only if" the consequent is true, it is meant that the consequent is a necessary condition.*

Let us now summarize the various guises under which statements of the form $P \supset Q$ appear in English. This can be done effectively in tabular form, as follows:

Statement with suggested notation	*"If ... then—" equivalent*	*Translation*
a. If this is a whale, then it is a mammal. (W, M)	If this is a whale, then it is a mammal.	W ⊃ M
b. If this is a whale, it's a mammal. (W, M)	If this is a whale, then it is a mammal.	W ⊃ M

Statement with suggested notation	*"If . . . then—" equivalent*	*Translation*
c. I would like Jones better if he would be more dependable. (LJ, MD)	If Jones would be more dependable, then I would like him better.	MD ⊃ LJ
d. If the boss fires me, this means I will be out of a job. (BF, OJ)	If the boss fires me, then I will be out of a job.	BF ⊃ OJ
e. The acceptance of Euclidean geometry implies the acceptance of a three-dimensional space. (EG, TD)	If Euclidean geometry is accepted, then one must accept a three-dimensional space.	EG ⊃ TD
f. Had it rained, the pavement would be wet. (R, PW)	If it had rained, then the pavement would be wet.	R ⊃ PW
g. The pavement would be wet had it rained. (W, R)	If it had rained, then the pavement would be wet.	R ⊃ W
h. Whenever Marie flies into a rage, this means one should be careful! (MF, C)	If Marie flies into a rage, then one should be careful.	MF ⊃ C
i. One should be careful whenever Marie flies into a rage. (C, MF)	If Marie flies into a rage, then one should be careful.	MF ⊃ C
j. A necessary condition for this to be a whale is that it be a mammal. (W, M)	If this is a whale, then it is a mammal.	W ⊃ M
k. That this is a mammal is a necessary condition for it to be a whale. (M, W)	If this is a whale, then it is a mammal.	W ⊃ M
l. This is a whale only if it's a mammal. (W, M)	If this is a whale, then it is a mammal.	W ⊃ M
m. Only if it's a mammal is this a whale. (M, W)	If this is a whale, then it is a mammal.	W ⊃ M
n. A sufficient condition for this to be a mammal is that it be a whale. (M, W)	If this is a whale, then it is a mammal.	W ⊃ M
o. That this is a whale is a sufficient condition for it to be a mammal. (W, M)	If this is a whale, then it is a mammal.	W ⊃ M

Exercises

GROUP A

51. Explain, in your own words, what is meant by "necessary condition". Illustrate with your own examples.
52. Explain, in your own words, what is meant by "sufficient condition". Illustrate with your own examples.
53. Explain, in your own words, the significance of the phrase "only if". Illustrate with your own examples.
54. Construct a table, like that at the end of this section, illustrating the variants of "if · · · then—" statements discussed. Give three columns, like the model table in the text, the first listing the variant with the notation you will use, the second giving the "if · · · then—" equivalent in English, and the third giving the symbolic translation. Be sure you cover every case given in the model table. Use entirely *original examples*.

GROUP B

For each of the English statements below, (a) rewrite into an English statement of the standard "if · · · then—" form; (b) translate into symbolic form, using the suggested notation. (Remember that the suggested variables are given in the same order as are the English atomic statements for which they stand. This order may need to be reversed in translating the molecular statements into symbolic form.)

55. Had it been natural for Copernicus to propose that the sun was the center of the universe, he would have supposed that the earth moved around the sun. (SC, EM)
56. Copernicus would have proposed that the sun was the center of the universe had he found that his system was vastly simpler than that of Ptolemy. (SC, SP)
57. He would suppose that the sun stood still if he supposed that the earth moved around it. (SS, EM)
58. His system was vastly simpler than that of Ptolemy only if it eliminated numerous epicycles. (SP, EE)
59. If we observe sun spots, this means that the substance of the sun is homogeneous with that of the earth. (OS, SH)
60. Jane is ill if she has a fever. (JI, HF)
61. Had Ptolemy realized how cumbrous his epicycles were, he would have proposed a heliocentric cosmology. (PR, HC)
62. If one holds a heliocentric cosmology, this implies that one believes the sun to be the center of the universe. (HC, SC)

63. That the earth is the center of the universe is a sufficient condition for a geocentric cosmology.   (EC, GC)
64. A necessary condition for holding a geocentric cosmology is to believe that the earth is the center of the universe.   (GC, EC)
65. A sufficient condition for Jones' death was his incurable cancer.   (JD, IC)
66. Cancer is incurable only if it causes the death of the patient.   (CI, DP)
67. That the patient will die is a necessary condition for him to have incurable cancer.   (PD, IC)
68. Had I had a toothache, I would have seen a dentist.   (T, D)
69. One should see a dentist whenever he has a toothache.   (D, T)
70. This is shredded wheat only if it is breakfast cereal.   (SW, BC)
71. The pavement will get wet whenever it rains.   (PW, R)
72. Only if causal inferences are justifiable can we predict the future.   (IJ, PF)
73. That the soul will survive the death of the body is a necessary condition for it to be immortal.   (SD, I)
74. A sufficient condition for Arthur to invite Grace to the dance is that he enjoys her company.   (IG, EC)
75. Socrates is mortal only if men are mortal.   (SM, MM)

§5.   Proofs for the Validity of Arguments

We learned earlier (in §3) how to recognize legitimate instances of A_1, which was, as we recall, the following form:

A_1 (*modus ponens*): $P \supset Q$
$\qquad\qquad\qquad\qquad P$
$\qquad\qquad\qquad\quad \therefore Q$

Sometimes an argument in English may have more than the two premises required by A_1; yet A_1 can be used to prove its validity. Consider, for example, the following argument in English:

EXAMPLE 16

> If students are sensible, they desire balanced diets. If students desire balanced diets, they should avoid campus hash-houses. Students are sensible. Therefore they should avoid campus hash-houses.   (SS, BD, AH)

Note that, according to our convention, the suggested notation is given in parentheses at the end of the argument, and that the variables suggested are given in the same order as that in which the atomic statements which they represent first appear in English.

To construct a formal proof for the validity of this argument, we first translate the premises *in the order in which they appear in English.* Some students, recognizing that the English formulation of an argument is not always as orderly as might be desired, have a tendency to rearrange the order of premises in their translations. But let us adhere meticulously to the convention of translating the premises in the order in which they appear in English. Then there will be no confusion as to which symbolic statement refers to which English statement. The three premises of our argument are translated, in order, as follows:

1. SS ⊃ BD
2. BD ⊃ AH
3. SS

In order that we may know the justification for each statement in a proof of the validity of an argument, let us, in the right-hand column, after each statement, *always give a reason for the statement.* In the case of statements 1, 2, and 3 in our proof, the reason is "Premise". Let us indicate this:

1. SS ⊃ BD   Premise
2. BD ⊃ AH   Premise
3. SS   Premise

Note that we have numbered each step in our proof. As the proof progresses, we shall have to refer back to earlier statements to justify later ones; and if each statement is numbered, we shall be able to refer to an earlier statement by number alone, instead of rewriting the entire statement.

So far, we have the first three statements of our proof of validity properly set up. From these premises we wish to conclude AH. Let us therefore, in order to know what we are striving to prove, make a sign like ╱_____ in the upper right-hand corner, and write in it ∴ AH. So far, our work should look like this:

╱ ∴ AH

1. SS ⊃ BD   Premise
2. BD ⊃ AH   Premise
3. SS   Premise

The problem now is, how, from statements 1, 2, and 3, can we arrive at the desired conclusion? In order to ascertain this, let us see what would be needed in order to conclude AH. In other words, let us proceed in reverse, from conclusion to premises, in what may be known as "the backward method of proving validity". Since A_1 is the only valid argument form presently at our disposal, let us draw a diagram for A_1, and indicate AH as the conclusion, marked by the arrow in Example 17:

EXAMPLE 17

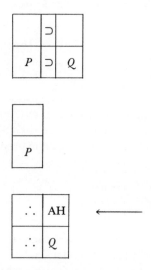

Note, further, that since AH is an instance of Q in the conclusion of A_1, it will also have to be an instance of Q in the first premise. Let us accordingly note this in our diagram:

EXAMPLE 18

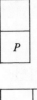

∴	AH
∴	Q

Now we see that, in order to conclude AH, we need an "if · · · then—" statement, the right-hand member of which is AH. Have we such a statement in the first three statements of our proof of validity? Yes, we do. Statement 2, in fact, is BD ⊃ AH. This tells us what else we can fill in in our diagram, namely BD for *P*:

EXAMPLE 19

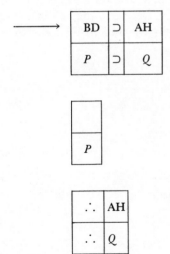

Further, since BD is taken as the instance of *P* in the first premise of A_1, it must be taken as the instance of *P* in the second premise. Let us indicate this:

EXAMPLE   20

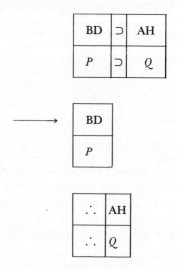

Now, returning to our proof, do we have BD, the second statement required by our diagram, so that we can conclude AH? We do not, but we can easily conclude it by applying A_1 to statements 1 and 3, thus:

EXAMPLE   21

Statement 1:

SS	⊃	BD
P	⊃	Q

Statement 3:

SS
P

∴	BD
∴	Q

We can now add BD as statement 4 of our proof, giving as a reason for the statement: "From 1, 3, and A_1". Our proof then appears as follows:

∠ ∴ AH

1. SS ⊃ BD   Premise
2. BD ⊃ AH   Premise
3. SS   Premise
4. BD   From 1, 3, and A_1

This gives us the BD required by the diagram of Example 20. We are now ready to conclude AH. We shall place the sign for conclusion (∴) before AH, and indicate as a reason for the statement: "From 2, 4, and A_1". Our completed proof of validity looks like this:

∠ ∴ AH

1. SS ⊃ BD   Premise
2. BD ⊃ AH   Premise
3. SS   Premise
4. BD   From 1, 3, and A_1
5. ∴ AH   From 2, 4, and A_1

Let us look at another short proof of validity, this time for the following argument:

Marie sees Herman. Whenever Marie sees Herman, this means look out! So, look out!   (SH, LO)

The proof for the validity of this argument follows:

∠ ∴ LO

1. SH   Premise
2. SH ⊃ LO   Premise
3. ∴ LO   From 2, 1, and A_1

Even in a three-statement argument like this, which is an obvious instance of A_1, *be sure to number each step and give a reason for it in the right-hand column.* If this convention is followed in even the simplest cases, confusion will not result in more complex ones.

With regard to this last example, attention should be called to the reason for statement 3, which is, "From 2, 1, and A_1". Why should not the reason be "From 1, 2, and A_1"? To answer this question, let us draw a diagram of A_1, and show how statements 1 and 2 of our proof fit into it:

EXAMPLE   22

Statement 2:

SH	⊃	LO
P	⊃	Q

Statement 1:

SH
P

∴	LO
∴	Q

Statement 2, as we see from the diagram, corresponds to the first premise of A_1, and statement 1 corresponds to the second premise. Hence the reason for LO is "From 2, 1, and A_1", not "From 1, 2, and A_1", which would indicate that statement 1 corresponds to the first premise of A_1, and statement 2 to the second; this of course is not the case. Again, meticulous care in such matters will prevent confusion later. Always be sure your reason for a statement indicates the exact replacement in the argument form used. Never hesitate to draw diagrams for yourself to make sure of exact replacement.

One final illustration of a proof for the validity of an argument follows:

Argument:
    I'll cut class. If I miss important work, I'll fail the course. If I cut class, I will miss important work. If I fail the course, my parents will cut off my financial support. If my parents cut off my financial support, I'll jump into the river. Therefore, I'll jump into the river.   (CC, MW, FC, CS, JR)

Proof of validity:

∴ JR

1. CC   Premise

2. MW ⊃ FC	Premise
3. CC ⊃ MW	Premise
4. FC ⊃ CS	Premise
5. CS ⊃ JR	Premise
6. MW	From 3, 1, and A$_1$
7. FC	From 2, 6, and A$_1$
8. CS	From 4, 7, and A$_1$
9. ∴ JR	From 5, 8, and A$_1$

EXERCISES

Construct a proof of validity for each of the following arguments, in each case using the notation suggested in parentheses:

76. If Kepler was right, then planetary motion is elliptical. Kepler was right. Therefore planetary motion is elliptical.   (KR, ME)

77. A necessary condition for Smith to be completely relaxed is that he will fall asleep easily. Smith is completely relaxed. Hence Smith will fall asleep easily.   (CR, FA)

78. A sufficient condition for Jones to fall asleep easily is that he be exhausted. Jones is exhausted. So Jones will fall asleep easily.   (FA, E)

79. Adams sleeps well only if he has had a hard day. Adams is sleeping well. Thus Adams has had a hard day.   (SW, HD)

80. Mary will fall asleep easily whenever she is tired. Mary is tired. Hence Mary will fall asleep easily.   (FA, T)

81. If Grace has pneumonia, she will have a fever. If she has a fever, then she will remain in bed. If she remains in bed, Arthur will have to get someone else to go to the theater with him. Grace has pneumonia. Therefore Arthur will have to get someone else to go to the theater with him.   (GP, HF, RB, AT)

82. Arthur invited Grace to the theater only if he bought two tickets. If he bought two tickets, this means he'll be short on cash till payday. He'll have to borrow money if he'll be short on cash till payday. Arthur invited Grace to the theater. Therefore he'll have to borrow money.   (IG, BT, SC, BM)

83. A sufficient condition for Copernicus to suppose that the earth moved around the sun was that he proposed that the sun was the center of the universe. He found that his system was vastly simpler than that of Ptolemy. He supposed that the earth moved around the sun only if he supposed that the sun stood still. A necessary condition for Copernicus to find that his system was vastly simpler than that of Ptolemy was that he proposed that the sun was the center of the universe. Hence he supposed that the sun stood still.   (EM, SC, SP, SS)

84. As Hutcheson supposed, we have a "moral sense" which accounts for our perception of virtue and vice. If we say that all men have a *similar* moral sense, then we can introduce a subjective universality into ethical judgments. If, as Hutcheson supposed, we have a moral sense which accounts for our perception of virtue and vice, then there arises the problem of ethical standards. We can say that all men have a *similar* moral sense if there arises the problem of ethical standards. Therefore we can introduce a subjective universality into ethical judgments.   (MS, SS, SU, PS)

85. If all our ideas come from sensation and reflection, substance is only a something "I know not what," as Locke put it. All our ideas do come from sensation and reflection, if the doctrine of innate ideas is absurd. The mind is, at first, like a "blank tablet." If the mind is, at first, like a "blank tablet," then the doctrine of innate ideas is absurd. Therefore substance is only a something "I know not what," as Locke put it.   (SR, SS, DA, BT)

§6.   The Fallacy of Affirming the Consequent

In some of the exercises at the end of §3, we encountered a few arguments which, rather than being instances of A_1, were instances of an *invalid* form somewhat resembling it. It is necessary to know and to recognize this invalid form so that we may avoid it. It is known as *"the fallacy of affirming the consequent"*, and is stated as follows:

> *Fallacy of Affirming the Consequent:* $P \supset Q$
> Q
> $\therefore P$

The term "fallacy" is used to designate any invalid argument form. This particular fallacy affirms, in its second premise, the consequent (i.e., the right-hand member) of the hypothetical conditional which constitutes its first premise. This explains the name of the fallacy, "the fallacy of affirming the consequent".

Let us illustrate why this fallacy is an invalid argument form, by analyzing an instance of it:

EXAMPLE   23

> If this substance is uranium, then it is radioactive.
> This substance is radioactive.
> Therefore this substance is uranium.

Let us assume that, as the first premise of this argument states, if a given substance is uranium, then it is radioactive. Now, if we know that the substance under consideration is in fact uranium, we could conclude, by A_1, that it is radioactive. However, our second premise does not state that the substance is uranium. It rather states that it is radioactive. And, from the fact that the substance is radioactive, we cannot conclude that it must be uranium. It might as well be plutonium or some other radioactive substance.

Let us offer another explanation of the fallaciousness of this form in terms of necessary and sufficient conditions. Consider the following argument:

EXAMPLE 24

If this is a whale, then it is a mammal.
This is a mammal.
Therefore it is a whale.

From our previous analysis of the first premise of this argument, we know that it means that being a whale is a sufficient condition for the animal under consideration to be a mammal, and that being a mammal is a necessary condition for it to be a whale. The fallacy of affirming the consequent affirms the necessary condition, and hence implies that the sufficient condition follows. In other words, it states that if the necessary condition is affirmed, then that for which it is necessary must follow. This, however, is obviously not the case, since the necessary condition could be necessary for other things besides whales. For example, it is necessary for something to be a mammal in order for it to be a cat, or a mouse, or a hamster, as well. Knowing that it is a mammal, there is no reason to assume that the animal is one of these rather than another.

Let us correct the fallacy of Example 24, and put forth the following legitimate instance of A_1:

EXAMPLE 25

If this is a whale, then it is a mammal.
This is a whale.
Therefore it is a mammal.

Now the second premise affirms the *sufficient* condition. And we know further, from the first premise, that being a mammal is a necessary condition for something to be a whale; i.e., that if it is a whale, it is necessary that it be a mammal; or again, that being a mammal necessarily follows from the fact of something being a whale. Hence the conclusion of this argument, namely that the thing talked about is a mammal, is justified.

EXERCISES

Which of these arguments are legitimate instances of A_1, and which are instances of the fallacy of affirming the consequent?

86. If it is going to rain, I will take an umbrella. I will take an umbrella. Hence it is going to rain.
87. I like this music if it's not too loud. I like this music. Therefore it's not too loud.
88. A necessary condition for this to be a dove is that it be a bird. This is a dove. Hence it is a bird.
89. I like Jones if he's not obnoxious. I like Jones. So he's not obnoxious.
90. That this is a bird is a necessary condition for it to be a crow. This is a crow. Hence it is a bird.
91. A necessary condition for Grace to enjoy this weekend is that Arthur take her to the dance. Arthur is taking her to the dance. Hence Grace will enjoy this weekend.
92. A sufficient condition for Jane to enjoy this weekend is that John invite her to the dance. Jane is going to enjoy this weekend. Consequently John will invite her to the dance.
93. Jane will go with John only if Arthur isn't going to invite her. Arthur isn't going to invite her. Accordingly Jane will go with John.
94. Grace should not confide in Jane if she doesn't wish a distorted story to reach Arthur. Grace doesn't want a distorted story to reach Arthur. Thus Grace should not confide in Jane.
95. Grace should not confide in Jane if she doesn't think she can trust her. She doesn't think she can trust Jane. Therefore Grace should not confide in Jane.

§7. Modus Tollens

We are now ready to consider another valid argument form. This form logicians call *"modus tollens"*; we shall designate it as "A_2". A preliminary statement of it follows:

If P, then Q
not-Q
Therefore not-P

This is not, of course, a completely symbolic statement of A_2. There is no difficulty putting the first premise into completely symbolic form, as we have done previously. But what about the second premise, and the conclusion? They involve the word "not". Let us introduce a symbol for negation, namely the sign $\sim$, called a *"tilde"*. The second premise of A_2 can now be written $\sim Q$, which will be read "not Q". Likewise, the conclusion of A_2 will be written $\therefore \sim P$. In completely symbolic notation then, A_2 is written as follows:

A_2: $P \supset Q$
$\sim Q$
$\therefore \sim P$

A word is in order about a convention that is generally used by logicians and that will be followed in this book, regarding the symbolic translation of negative statements. The suggested notation will always be given without the tilde; if the English statement is negative, the tilde must be added by the student in his translation. For example, if we have a statement such as "It is not raining", and R is the suggested notation, then R will be taken to represent the positive statement, "It is raining", and $\sim$ R will be the translation of the negative statement, "It is *not* raining."

Let us illustrate the validity of A_2 in terms of the following instance of it:

EXAMPLE 26

If this substance is uranium, then it is radioactive.
This substance is not radioactive.
Therefore this substance is not uranium.

The second premise in Example 26 denies of the substance under consideration the necessary condition under which it would be uranium. Hence, in the absence of this necessary condition, we can conclude that the substance is not uranium.

Let us state this differently using the phrase "only if". The first premise of the argument of Example 26 asserts that the substance is uranium only if it is radioactive. But since it is not radioactive (according to the second premise), it accordingly is not uranium (as the conclusion asserts).

A proof for the validity of an argument involving A_2 is constructed in exactly the same way as for one involving A_1 alone. Let us illustrate by means of a few examples. First, let us consider the following argument:

EXAMPLE   27

If Jane is waiting for Arthur to invite her to the dance this Saturday night, then Grace will be jealous. Grace will not be jealous. If Jane told John she already had a date for Saturday night, then she is waiting for Arthur to invite her. Consequently Jane didn't tell John she already had a date for Saturday night.   (WA, GJ, TJ)

The validity of this argument is proved as follows:

$$/ \therefore \sim TJ$$

1. WA ⊃ GJ   Premise
2. ~GJ   Premise
3. TJ ⊃ WA   Premise
4. ~WA   From 1, 2, and A_2
5. ∴ ~TJ   From 3, 4, and A_2

A_2 was the only valid argument form necessary to prove the validity of this argument. In the following proof of validity, however, both A_1 and A_2 are used:

EXAMPLE 28

If I do my homework, I am not going to get low grades. I do my homework. I'll fail the course only if I shall get low grades. Hence I won't fail the course.   (H, LG, FC)

The proof of the validity of this argument follows:

$$/ \therefore \sim FC$$

1. H ⊃ ~LG   Premise
2. H   Premise
3. FC ⊃ LG   Premise
4. ~LG   From 1, 2, and A_1
5. ∴ ~FC   From 3, 4, and A_2

We shall show, by means of diagrams indicating exact replacement in the two forms used (A_1 and A_2), how statements 4 and 5 of this proof were derived.

EXAMPLE 29

To Get Statement 4:

Form Used: A_1

Statement 1:

H	⊃	~LG
P	⊃	Q

Statement 2:

H
P

∴	~LG
∴	Q

EXAMPLE 30

To Get Statement 5:

Form Used: A_2

Statement 3:

FC	⊃	LG
P	⊃	Q

Statement 4:

~	LG
~	Q

∴	~	FC
∴	~	P

Note that any statement, atomic or molecular, may be taken as an instance of P, Q, etc., in our valid argument forms, as long as the replacement is uniform throughout the instance of the argument form. Thus, in Example 29, ~LG, which is a molecular statement consisting of the atomic statement LG and a tilde, is uniformly taken as an instance of Q. In Example 30, since an entirely different argument form is being considered, Q may be replaced by something different, as long as replacement is uniform throughout the instance of the argument form used. In Example 30, in fact, LG (without the tilde) is taken as an instance of Q, whereas ~LG is taken as the instance of Q in Example 29.

Example 29 illustrates that the mere presence of a tilde does not necessarily indicate that A_2 is to be used. A_1 (and, as we shall see later, even more forms) might be called for. The safest way to ascertain which forms to use and what replacements to make in the forms is to use the "backward method of proving validity," explained earlier; and to make diagrams showing exact replacements.

For the argument under consideration (see Example 28), the diagrams have already been given. Let us show how the backward method here applies in proving validity. From the premises (shown in Example 28), we must establish the conclusion ∴ ~FC. This could be got from statement 3 by means of A_2 if we had another statement ~LG (see Example 30). And in fact we can get this other statement ~LG directly by applying A_1 to statements 1 and 2 (see Example 29). Accordingly, we begin our proof by deriving ~LG from premises 1 and 2, and then continue by concluding ∴ ~FC from premise 3 and the ~LG which we have just obtained.

EXERCISES

GROUP A

96. What is the correct name for A_2?
97. Give the symbolic statement of A_2.

98. Construct five instances, in English, of A_2. Diagram them to show that they are legitimate instances.

99. Is ~LG an atomic or a molecular statement? Why?

GROUP B

Construct a proof for the validity of each of the following arguments, using the suggested notation.

100. If Grace has pneumonia, then she has a fever. Grace does not have a fever. Therefore she does not have pneumonia.   (GP, HF)

101. In order for the pavement to be wet, it is sufficient that someone emptied a bucket of water on it. The pavement is not wet. Hence it is not the case that someone emptied a bucket of water on it.   (PW, EB)

102. For Jones to play the piano well, it is necessary that he practice arduously. Jones does not practice arduously. Therefore he doesn't play the piano well.   (PP, PA)

103. If the earth is the center of the universe, then Tycho Brahe was right. If the earth is not the center of the universe, then Kepler was right. Tycho Brahe was not right. Thus Kepler was right.   (EC, TR, KR)

104. If the sun is the center of the universe, then Tycho Brahe was not right. If the earth is the center of the universe, then Tycho Brahe *was* right. The sun is the center of the universe. Hence the earth is *not* the center of the universe.   (SC, TR, EC)

105. If Arthur bought two tickets to the theater he will not have enough money to last him till payday. If Arthur is frugal, he will have enough money to last him till payday. Arthur bought two tickets to the theater. Therefore Arthur is not frugal.   (BT, HM, AF)

106. As Protagoras said, "Man is the measure of all things." If man is the measure of all things, as Protagoras said, then it is not certain what standards can be established. If ethical judgments are universal, it *is* certain what standards can be established. Therefore ethical judgments are *not* universal.   (MM, CS, JU)

107. The soul cannot occupy space. If the seat of the soul is the pineal gland, as Descartes supposed, then the problem of the interaction of soul and body is easily explained. The problem of the interaction of soul and body is not easily explained if the soul cannot occupy space. Therefore the seat of the soul is not, as Descartes supposed, the pineal gland.   (OS, PG, PE)

108. If Descartes was right, the ontological proof for the existence of God is valid. If Descartes was *not* right, then his vortex theory is not valid. His vortex theory *is* valid if Descartes' atomism is correct. The ontological proof for the existence of God is not valid. Thus Descartes' atomism is not correct.   (DR, PV, VV, AC)

109. Democritus thought atoms and the void constituted the ultimate nature of the universe. If he had held an opposite theory, he would have thought that colors and sounds had absolute existence. If Democritus thought atoms and the void constituted the ultimate nature of the universe, he would *not* have thought that colors and sounds had absolute existence. If he had not held an opposite theory, then he might truly be said to be the father of modern atomic theory. Therefore Democritus might truly be said to be the father of modern atomic theory.   (AV, OT, CS, FA)

110. It is not true that all men are hedonists. Aristotle's opponents are correct only if one can possess too much of the virtues of the intellect. That Aristotle was not wrong is a sufficient condition for the fact that one cannot possess too much of the virtues of the intellect. That all men are hedonists is a necessary condition for Aristotle being wrong. The theories of Aristotle's opponents should not be given credence if these opponents are not correct. Hence the theories of Aristotle's opponents should not be given credence.   (MH, OC, PV, AW, GC)

§8. The Fallacy of Denying the Antecedent

Just as we discovered an invalid argument form (the fallacy of affirming the consequent) which had carefully to be distinguished from A_1, so there is an invalid argument form which must carefully be distinguished from A_2. This is *the fallacy of denying the antecedent*.

> *Fallacy of Denying the Antecedent:* $P \supset Q$
> $\sim P$
> $\therefore \sim Q$

The fallacy derives its name from the fact that the second premise denies the antecedent (i.e., the left-hand member) of the hypothetical conditional (or "if . . . then—" statement) which constitutes the first premise. Let us illustrate its invalidity by means of an instance of it:

EXAMPLE 31

> If this substance is uranium, then it is radioactive.
> This substance is not uranium.
> Therefore this substance is not radioactive.

The first premise of this argument states that being uranium is only a sufficient, and not a necessary, condition for the substance to be radioactive. Even though the second premise denies the sufficient condition, other conditions would also be sufficient for the substance to be radioactive, e.g., if it were plutonium. If indeed the substance were plutonium, then the conclusion that the substance is not radioactive would be false.

This fallacy must not be confused with the valid argument form A_2, in which the second premise (as explained earlier) denies a *necessary* condition.

EXERCISES

State which of the following are instances of A_1, which are instances of A_2, which are instances of the fallacy of affirming the consequent, and which are instances of the fallacy of denying the antecedent.

111. If Copernicus was right, Ptolemy was wrong. Ptolemy was wrong. Hence Copernicus was right.

112. Copernicus was right only if Ptolemy was wrong. Copernicus was not right. Hence Ptolemy was not wrong.

113. Jane is ill whenever she has a fever. She doesn't have a fever. So she's not ill.

114. A sufficient condition for Jane to be ill is that she have a fever. Jane has a fever. Hence Jane is ill.

115. That Jane is ill is a necessary condition for her to have a fever. Jane is not ill. Hence Jane does not have a fever.

116. Aristotle should have thought some men were immortal if he believed in Greek mythology. Aristotle didn't believe in Greek mythology. Therefore he shouldn't have thought some men were immortal.

117. Aristotle held that Forms do not have existence apart from particular objects only if he rejected the Platonic doctrine of Ideas. Aristotle rejected the Platonic doctrine of Ideas. Consequently Aristotle held that Forms do not have existence apart from particular objects.

118. A necessary condition for Aristotle's classification of virtues into moral and intellectual was his twofold division of the soul. Aristotle divided the soul into two parts. Therefore he divided virtues into moral and intellectual.

119. For Jones to feel refreshed in the morning, it is sufficient that he get eight hours' sleep. Jones felt refreshed this morning. So he got eight hours' sleep.

120. Professor Brown advocates Schopenhauer's philosophy only if he is a pessimist. Professor Brown does not advocate Schopenhauer's philosophy. Therefore he is not a pessimist.

121. For Grace to go shopping tomorrow, a necessary condition is that it will be clear. It will not be clear tomorrow. Therefore Grace will not go shopping tomorrow.

122. For Jane to shop tomorrow, a sufficient condition is that she have a charge account. Jane will not shop tomorrow. Thus she does not have a charge account.

123. Butler was correct. That conscience is the supreme authority in moral conduct is a necessary condition for Butler to be correct. Hence conscience is the supreme authority in moral conduct.

124. Butler was correct only if conscience is the supreme authority in moral conduct. Conscience is the supreme authority in moral conduct. Hence Butler was correct.

125. Butler was not correct. That Butler was correct is a sufficient condition for conscience to be the supreme moral authority. Hence conscience is not the supreme moral authority.

§9. The Hypothetical Syllogism

Let us now introduce our third valid argument form, known to logicians as the "hypothetical syllogism". It is stated as follows:

A_3: $P \supset Q$
$\quad\ \ Q \supset R$
$\quad\ \ \therefore P \supset R$

What this argument form asserts is that if P is a sufficient condition for Q, and Q is a sufficient condition for R, then P is a sufficient condition for R. Or, again, if R is a necessary condition for Q (second premise), and Q is a necessary condition for P (first premise), then R is a necessary condition for P.

The addition of this new form, which we shall designate "A_3", to our repertoire of valid argument forms brings us to the point in the development of our logic where alternate proofs for the validity of a given argument are sometimes possible. Consider, for example, the following argument:

EXAMPLE 32

If Grace can not go to the dance, Arthur will ask Jane to accompany him. Jane will go to the dance with Arthur if he will ask her to accompany him. Grace cannot go to the dance. Consequently Jane will go to the dance with Arthur.   (GD, AJ, JG)

Two possible proofs for the validity of this argument follow:

EXAMPLE 33

First Proof

$/ \therefore JG$

1. $\sim$GD $\supset$ AJ   Premise
2. AJ $\supset$ JG   Premise
3. $\sim$GD   Premise
4. AJ   From 1, 3, and A_1
5. $\therefore$ JG   From 2, 4, and A_1

EXAMPLE 34

Second Proof

$/ \therefore JG$

1. $\sim$GD $\supset$ AJ   Premise
2. AJ $\supset$ JG   Premise
3. $\sim$GD   Premise
4. $\sim$GD $\supset$ JG   From 1, 2, and A_3
5. $\therefore$ JG   From 4, 3, and A_1

Both proofs are, in this case, equally correct and acceptable. Further, they both involve the same number of statements. Later, we shall encounter alternate proofs with differing numbers of statements. Then we shall choose the proof which is shortest.

EXERCISES

Using the three valid argument forms which you now know, construct a proof for the validity of each of the following arguments. The notation is suggested in parentheses at the end of each problem.

126. If Grace doesn't return from her trip, Arthur will lose interest in her. If Arthur loses interest in her, Grace will be unhappy. Therefore, if Grace doesn't return from her trip, she will be unhappy.   (GR, AL, GU)

127. If f is a function of x, then we may say that x has the property f. f is a function of x whenever f is a function of any variable. Therefore we may say that x has the property f whenever f is a function of any variable.   (FX, XF, FV)

128. If Arthur is not frugal, he will buy the tickets. If he buys the tickets, he will not have enough money to last him till payday. Therefore, if Arthur is not frugal, he will not have enough money to last him till payday. (AF, BT, HM)

129. If people fall on the slippery pavement they will break bones. If they break bones, they will have to miss work. If they miss work, they will lose money. Hence, if people fall on the slippery pavement they will lose money. (PF, BB, MW, LM)

130. If Grace is returning, she can accompany Arthur to the theater. If she can accompany Arthur to the theater, he won't mind being broke. If he won't mind being broke, this means he is not losing interest in Grace. Grace is returning. Hence Arthur is not losing interest in Grace.   (GR, AA, MB, LI)

131. A substance is radioactive only if it is dangerous. A sufficient condition for the radioactivity of a substance is that it be uranium. One should avoid a substance if it is dangerous. Hence whenever a substance is uranium one should avoid it.   (R, D, U, A)

132. If Arthur put Jane up to sending Grace a get-well card during her recent illness, he didn't think Jane would think of it herself. If Jane sent Grace a get-well card, Arthur put her up to it. Jane sent Grace a get-well card. If Arthur didn't think Jane would think of it herself, he does not think very highly of her. Hence Arthur does not think very highly of Jane. (PU, TJ, SC, TH)

133. A necessary condition for Jones' baldness is that he is not absorbing a sufficient supply of inositol. A sufficient condition for him to absorb a sufficient supply of inositol is that all the other B-complex vitamins be present in abundance in his diet. If he eats a nutritionally adequate diet, then all the other B-complex vitamins are present in abundance in his diet. Jones is bald. Therefore he does not eat a nutritionally adequate diet.   (JB, I, BP, AD)

134. A sufficient condition for Jane to be pleased is that John roast the wieners at the picnic. He will light the fire if he ignites the match. A sufficient condition for John to ignite the match is that he strike it. He will roast the wieners if he lights the fire. Therefore Jane will be pleased if John strikes the match.   (JP, RW, LF, IM, SM)

135. If Grace is going to see Arthur despite her mother's wishes, her mother is bound to find out. If her mother is bound to find out, she will tell Arthur to stay away. Arthur isn't going to do anything rash. If Grace's mother is going to forbid her to see Arthur, she is going to see him despite her mother's wishes. If Grace's mother tells Arthur to stay away, he is going to do something rash. Accordingly Grace's mother isn't going to forbid her to see Arthur.   (S, MB, TA, R, FS)

§10. The Disjunctive Syllogism and the Commutativity of Disjunction

A disjunctive statement is a statement of the form *"P or Q"*. Actually, the English word "or" is ambiguous; sometimes it means "and/or", and sometimes it means "either . . . or . . . but not both". In the first sense, in which at least one of the disjuncts (these being the statements on each side of the "or") is true, and in which the possibility that both may be true is not excluded, we say that the "or" is "an *inclusive* disjunction". In the second case, in which it is asserted that only one of the disjuncts is true, the "or" is referred to as "an *exclusive* disjunction".

If someone says "You can buy typewriter ribbons at Woolworth's or at Kresge's", he is using an *inclusive* disjunction, and probably does not mean to imply that you can't buy typewriter ribbons at Woolworth's and at Kresge's. Probably you won't buy one at Woolworth's and then get another at Kresge's, but you very well could. All that the *inclusive* disjunctive statement implies is that one or the other *and perhaps both* stores carry typewriter ribbons.

On the other hand, if someone says that his typewriter is either a standard or a portable, he is using an *exclusive* disjunction, since no typewriter can be both a portable and a standard machine at the same time.

We shall consider disjunctive statements of the *exclusive* variety later, but for the present we shall consider the *inclusive* type. In order clearly to designate this usage, we shall introduce the symbol V, called the *"wedge"*, to indicate the *inclusive* disjunction. The *exclusive* disjunction, which we shall discuss later, will be represented by a different symbol. Thus logic, by the use of two different symbols for the two different senses of "or", can avoid the ambiguity inherent in the English word itself. Only occasionally, to avoid this ambiguity of ordinary language, do people bother to designate the inclusive sense of "or" clearly by some such device as "and/or"; usually they rely on context to indicate which sense of "or" is intended. Logic, with its unambiguous symbol V can neatly indicate the inclusive sense of "or" without relying on the uncertainty of context, simply by writing $P \lor Q$. In the exercises in this chapter, the word "or" will always refer to the *inclusive* disjunction. The other sense of "or" will be considered in Chapter Three.

There is a logical principle known sometimes as the *"disjunctive syllogism"*, and sometimes as the *"principle of alternation"*, which involves disjunctive statements of the inclusive type. What is involved in the principle is this: If we are given an inclusive disjunction, of the form $P \lor Q$, and are further given that one disjunct is not the case, then we may conclude that the other disjunct is the case.

This principle we may formulate into the following valid argument form:

A_4: $P \lor Q$
       $\sim P$
       $\therefore Q$

With the addition of this new form to our list of valid argument forms, we can easily prove the validity of an argument like the following:

EXAMPLE 35

Grace is going shopping or she will meet Arthur. She is not going shopping. Hence she will meet Arthur.

But consider the following argument:

EXAMPLE 36

Grace is going shopping or she will meet Arthur. She will not meet Arthus. Hence she will go shopping.

A_4 cannot be used to prove the validity of the argument of Example 36 inasmuch as in this argument the *second* disjunct is denied, whereas A_4 permits only the denial of the *first* disjunct. In order to prove the validity of the argument of Example 36, we shall have to introduce another valid argument form. We could introduce the form:

$$P \lor Q$$
$$\sim Q$$
$$\therefore P$$

Instead, however, we shall introduce a form which will later enable us to do considerably more than this suggested form. The form which we shall introduce instead is this:

A_5: $P \lor Q$
       $\therefore Q \lor P$

A_5 is called "the principle of commutativity of the inclusive disjunction". A logical operation is called "a *commutative* operation" if, and only if, the result of the operation is independent of the order of the statements involved. Students of mathematics will be familiar with the following identities expressing commutativity:

1. $(a + b) = (b + a)$
2. $(a \times b) = (b \times a)$

However, let it be noted that not all logical operations are commutative, just as not all mathematical operations are. Subtraction is not commutative; i.e., $a - b$ is not the same as $b - a$. Division also is not commutative; that is to say $a \div b$ is not the same as $b \div a$. So, in logic, implication is not commutative; in other words, $P \supset Q$ is not the same as $Q \supset P$, as will be readily realized by reflecting on the properties of necessary and sufficient conditions.

EXERCISES

GROUP A

136. What principle is represented by A_4?
137. What principle is represented by A_5?
138. If A_5 were not included in our system of logic, what other valid argument form would have to be introduced to prove the validity of arguments of the form:

$$P \lor Q$$
$$\sim Q$$
$$\therefore P$$

139. Distinguish between the inclusive and exclusive senses of "or".

GROUP B

Which of the following expressions admit of commutativity? In each case, give a reason. If there is any ambiguity, indicate this.

140. A is identical to B.
141. A is like B.
142. A is as old as B.
143. A is larger than B.
144. A is the brother of B.
145. A is the sibling of B.
146. A is the twin of B.
147. A is beside B.
148. A is to the left of B.
149. A is near B.
150. A is as tall as B.
151. A implies B.
152. Either A or B, but not both.
153. A and B.
154. A is better than B.
155. A is older than B.

GROUP C

Using the valid argument forms now at your disposal, construct a proof for the validity of each of the following arguments, using the suggested notation.

156. Sergei likes Tschaikowsky or he likes Stravinsky. Sergei does not like Tschaikowsky. Therefore he likes Stravinsky.   (LT, LS)

157. Sergei likes Stravinsky or he likes Rimsky-Korsakov. Sergei does not like Rimsky-Korsakov. Hence Sergei likes Stravinsky.   (LS, LR)

158. If Sergei doesn't like Liszt, then he doesn't like Chopin. He doesn't like Liszt or he likes Schubert. He doesn't like Schubert. Hence Sergei doesn't like Chopin.   (LL, LC, LS)

159. If Sergei likes Chopin, then he likes Grieg. He doesn't like Grieg. If he doesn't like Chopin, then he doesn't like Mendelssohn. He likes Mendelssohn or he likes Stravinsky. Hence he likes Stravinsky.   (LC, LG, LM, LS)

160. If Arthur takes Jane on the hayride, Grace will be distraught. Either Arthur takes Jane on the hayride, or he takes Grace. Grace will not be distraught. If Arthur takes Grace on the hayride, Jane will not be happy. Either Grace will be happy or Jane will be happy. Therefore Grace will be happy.   (TJ, GD, TG, JH, GH)

161. If Grace goes on the hayride, her mother will worry that she may get pneumonia again. If her mother will worry that Grace may get pneumonia again, then she will think ill of Arthur. Either Grace goes on the hayride or Arthur will invite Jane. Arthur will not invite Jane. Therefore Grace's mother will think ill of Arthur.   (GH, MW, TI, IJ)

162. Grace's mother will be furious only if it is going to snow. Either Grace's mother will be furious or Grace will get permission to go on the hayride. It is not going to snow. If Grace gets her mother's permission to go on the hayride, Arthur will not be disappointed. Either Arthur will be disappointed or he will enjoy the hayride. Therefore Arthur will enjoy the hayride.   (MF, S, GP, AD, EH)

163. Grace and Arthur will not go skiing if it's not going to snow. John and Jane will go skiing only if Grace and Arthur go. Either John and Jane visit some friends or they will go skiing. It's not going to snow. If John and Jane visit some friends, Jane will be bored. Therefore Jane will be bored.   (GA, S, JJ, VF, JB)

164. Grace will not get pneumonia again. Either Arthur trusts Jane, or he merely enjoys her vivacity. If Arthur trusts Jane, then Grace will trust Jane. If Grace is careless, she will get pneumonia again. Grace will be careless if she is foolish. If Grace has some common sense, then she will not trust Jane. Either Grace has some common sense or she is foolish. Thus Arthur merely enjoys Jane's vivacity.   (GP, AT, EV, GT, GC, GF, CS)

165. Grace's mother is trying to prevent Grace from seeing Arthur only if she is not wise. Grace's mother is trying to prevent Grace from seeing Arthur. Either Grace's mother is wise or she does not realize how serious Grace and Arthur are. Either she is not perceptive or she does realize how serious Grace and Arthur are. Hence Grace's mother is not perceptive.   (TP, W, RS, P)

§11.   Atomic and Molecular Statements

We said earlier that the smallest statement-units are called *"atomic statements"*, and that any compound statement is a *molecular* statement. Thus we say that $\sim P$ is a molecular statement form with an atomic component P. Likewise, $P \supset Q$ and $P \vee Q$ are molecular statement forms with two atomic components, P and Q. We have noted further that a molecular statement may be taken as an instance of an atomic statement in any of our valid argument forms. Thus, taking H as an instance of P and taking the molecular statement $\sim$LG as an instance of Q, we saw that the following is a legitimate instance of A_1 (see Example 28):

$$H \supset \sim LG$$
$$H$$
$$\therefore \sim LG$$

Even more complex statements than that of the form $\sim P$ can be taken as an instance of an atomic variable in our valid argument forms. Thus, all of the following could be taken as instances of P:

EXAMPLE   37

1. $(A \supset B) \vee (C \supset D)$
2. $A \supset \sim[B \vee (C \supset D)]$
3. $(A \vee B) \supset \{[(C \vee D) \vee \sim E] \supset F\}$

Let us look at these three statements, and make some remarks about them.

Statement 1 could be taken as a simple instance of any atomic variable in any of our valid argument forms. For example, it could be used in A_1 in the following manner:

$$[(A \supset B) \vee (C \supset D)] \supset X$$
$$(A \supset B) \vee (C \supset D)$$
$$\therefore X$$

Here it is taken as an instance of P in A_1, as the following diagram clearly indicates:

EXAMPLE   38

$[(A \supset B) \vee (C \supset D)]$	$\supset$	X
P	$\supset$	Q

$(A \supset B) \vee (C \supset D)$
P

$\therefore$	X
$\therefore$	Q

In this instance of A_1, the statement under consideration is placed in square brackets in the first premise to indicate that the entire statement implies X. Stated singly, as in the second premise, the statement does not require the square brackets.

By itself, statement 1 of Example 37 is merely a disjunctive statement of the inclusive type, and could be taken as an instance of $P \vee Q$, as the following diagram indicates:

$(A \supset B)$	$\vee$	$(C \supset D)$
P	$\vee$	Q

Consider for a moment statement 2 of Example 37. This whole statement could be taken as an instance of P or as an instance of $P \supset Q$, since it basically is a hypothetical conditional (i.e., a statement of the form "if $\cdots$ then—"). Further, note that the tilde, since it precedes the brackets, negates the entire disjunctive statement within the brackets.

Brackets are used to indicate a statement which contains within it a molecular statement enclosed in parentheses, as in statement 2 of Example 37. If the bracketed statement is itself part of a larger statement, braces will be used to indicate the larger quantity, as in statement 3 of Example 37. The order, then, of parentheses, brackets, and braces obtains from smaller to larger units, thus:

$$\{ \ [\ (\ ) \ ] \ \}$$

The parentheses, brackets, and braces are the punctuation marks of symbolic logic, and serve to eliminate ambiguity. Thus, as in English, we distinguish different meanings by the use of punctuation, so do we in logic. For example, observe the following two English statements and their corresponding symbolic translations:

EXAMPLE   39

    a. If John gets home early, then we will have an $HE \supset (ED \lor EO)$
       early dinner or else we will eat out.
    b. If John gets home early, then we will have an $(HE \supset ED) \lor EO$
       early dinner; or else we will eat out.

Let us show, by means of an argument in English, how we can prove the validity of an argument involving molecular statements. The argument whose validity we wish to prove follows:

EXAMPLE   40

If pleasure is the good, then either the Epicureans are wrong or the Stoics are wrong. If either the Epicureans are wrong or the Stoics are wrong, error pervades philosophy. Error does not pervade philosophy. Therefore, pleasure is not the good.   (PG, EW, SW, EP)

Here is the proof of its validity:

EXAMPLE   41

$$\diagup \therefore \ \sim PG$$

1. $PG \supset (EW \lor SW)$	Premise
2. $(EW \lor SW) \supset EP$	Premise
3. $\sim EP$	Premise

4. ~(EW ∨ SW)   From 2, 3, and A$_2$
5. ∴ ~PG   From 1, 4, and A$_2$

We shall show, by means of diagrams, how statements 4 and 5 of this proof were got:

EXAMPLE   42

To Get Statement 4:

Form Used: A$_2$

Statement 2:

(EW ∨ SW)	⊃	EP
P	⊃	Q

Statement 3:

~	EP
~	Q

∴	~	(EW ∨ SW)
∴	~	P

EXAMPLE   43

To Get Statement 5:

Form Used: A$_2$

Statement 1:

PG	⊃	(EW ∨ SW)
P	⊃	Q

Statement 4:

~	(EW ∨ SW)
~	Q

As long as diagrams are used whenever doubt is incurred as to what replacements are to be made in a given form, no confusion will result with the introduction of more complex statements. Thus, for example, given ∼(∼X ∨ ∼Y), we can not indiscriminately remove parentheses and arrive at some such statement as ∼ ∼X ∨ ∼ ∼Y, although some students are tempted to do this by analogy with the mathematical operation of "multiplying through". The inference from ∼(∼X ∨ ∼Y) to ∼ ∼X ∨ ∼ ∼Y is fallacious, and cannot be put into a diagram for any of our valid argument forms. The first tilde in the original statement negates the *entire* statement ∼X ∨ ∼Y. Since the tilde is not the same as the mathematical *minus* sign, and since the first tilde does not cover each part of the statement in parentheses *separately*, the notion of "multiplying through" does not apply.

Similarly, given ∼(P ⊃ Q), we can not "multiply through" and get ∼P ⊃ ∼Q. Consider an example: "It is not true that if it rains, Grace will go shopping"—an instance of ∼(P ⊃ Q)—is clearly not equivalent to "Grace won't go shopping if it doesn't rain"—an instance of ∼P ⊃ ∼Q.

Think, then, in terms of *logical*, not of *mathematical*, operations; and when in doubt, draw diagrams.

EXERCISES

Construct a proof for the validity of each of the following arguments, using the suggested notation:

166. Jones can not start his tractor easily. If Jones covers his tractor with a tarpaulin whenever it rains, then his tractor will stay dry. If his tractor stays dry, then he can start it easily. Therefore it is not the case that Jones covers his tractor with a tarpaulin whenever it rains. (SE, CT, R, SD)

167. A necessary condition for Grace to like the theater production is that she like Gertrude Stein. She does not like Gertrude Stein. If Grace doesn't like the theater production, Arthur will feel like a fool if he spent his last penny for the tickets. Arthur spent his last penny for the tickets. Hence Arthur will feel like a fool. (TP, LS, AF, SP)

168. A sufficient condition for Copernicus to propose a heliocentric cosmology is that it eliminated numerous epicycles of the Ptolemaic system. If Copernicus proposed a heliocentric cosmology, then either Tycho or Kepler was on the wrong track. The Copernican system eliminated numerous epicycles of the Ptolemaic system. Kepler was not on the wrong track. Hence Tycho was on the wrong track.   (HC, EE, T, K)

169. Either the doctrine of occasionalism is false; or if Berkeley was right, objects are merely ideas. If objects are not merely ideas, then Malebranche was correct. If Malebranche was correct, then the doctrine of occasionalism is not false. Objects are not merely ideas. Therefore Berkeley was not right.   (DF, BR, OI, MC)

170. Geometers follow the system of Riemann or they adhere to Euclid's *Elements*. If they follow the system of Riemann, then either they think Euclidean geometry is an equally useful alternative or they find Riemannian geometry more workable for astronomical space. Either they do not adhere to Euclid's *Elements* or they think Euclidean geometry is an equally useful alternative to Riemannian geometry. Geometers do not think Euclidean geometry is an equally useful alternative to Riemannian geometry. Hence they find Riemannian geometry more workable for astronomical space.   (FR, AE, EU, MW)

171. Mankind is not patient. If the law of parity has been disproved, this means that either science is absolutely incapable of establishing truth or truth is established slowly. It is not true that science is absolutely incapable of establishing truth. If truth is established slowly, then mankind shall possess absolute truth only if it is patient. The law of parity has been disproved. Consequently mankind shall not possess absolute truth.   (MP, LD, SI, TS, PT)

172. If the pavement will be slippery whenever it rains; then if people fall on the slippery pavement, they may break bones. The pavement will be slippery if it gets wet. The pavement will get wet if it rains. Therefore, if people fall on the slippery pavement, they may break bones.   (PS, R, PF, BB, GW)

173. If all types of food are plentiful, then if people have money they will be sensible in their purchases of food. All types of food are plentiful or our economists deceive us. If our economists deceive us, then they are frauds. Our economists are not frauds. If people are sensible in their purchases of food, they will eat balanced diets. Therefore, if people have money, they will eat balanced diets.   (FP, HM, SP, ED, EF, BD)

174. Either we leave the water on, or we turn it off if it freezes. If we leave the water on, we will be sorry. Either we won't be sorry or we will be prepared. We will find ourselves without water only if we are not prepared. We will find ourselves without water. If we turn off the water our pipes

will be safe. Consequently, if it freezes, our pipes will be safe.   (LO, TO, F, S, P, WW, PS)

175. If Sergei likes Bach, then if he likes the harpsichord he likes Bach on the harpsichord. If Sergei is discriminating, then if he likes Bach on the harpsichord he will not like Bach on the piano. If Sergei is a sensitive musician, he likes Bach. Sergei is discriminating if he doesn't like Chaminade. If he likes Chaminade, then he likes von Suppé. Either he doesn't like von Suppé or he likes Grieg. Sergei is a sensitive musician. He doesn't like Grieg. Hence, if he likes the harpsichord, he will not like Bach on the piano.   (LB, LH, BH, SD, BP, SM, LC, VS, LG)

§12.   The Constructive Dilemma

The sixth valid argument form which we shall introduce is known as the *"constructive dilemma"*. It is stated as follows:

A_6: $P \supset Q$
$R \supset S$
$P \lor R$
$\therefore Q \lor S$

In order to understand this form, which we shall refer to as "A_6", let us think of the hypothetical conditionals which form the first two premises in terms of their antecedents (left-hand members) and consequents (right-hand members). The antecedents we shall designate by the symbols, a and a', and the consequents by c and c'. The first two premises, then, become:

$$a \supset c$$
$$a' \supset c'$$

The third premise of A_6 tells us that at least one of the antecedents of our two hypothetical conditionals is true. Symbolically, we represent this as follows:

$$a \lor a'$$

It therefore follows that at least one of the consequents of our two hypothetical conditionals is true, i.e.:

$$\therefore c \lor c'$$

We can also explain A_6 in terms of necessary and sufficient conditions. If we are given two hypothetical conditionals (premises 1 and 2 of A_6), and are further given that at least one of the antecedents of these hypothetical conditionals is true (premise 3), here is what we can conclude: The necessary condition for the first antecedent will be true if the first antecedent is true, and the necessary condition for the second antecedent will be true if the second antecedent is true. Now, since we know that at least one of the antecedents is true, it follows that at least one of their necessary conditions is true, which is what the conclusion of A_6 states.

Let us give an example in English to illustrate A_6:

EXAMPLE   44

> If the weather is clear, I shall go downtown today.
> If it is raining, I shall stay home.
> The weather is clear or it is raining.
> Therefore I shall go downtown today or I shall stay home.

With the introduction of A_6 into our logic, we have reached the point at which two alternate proofs for the validity of an argument may differ in the number of statements involved. In such cases, the shorter proof is preferable, on the grounds of what the logician calls *"elegance"*, i.e., brevity or simplicity of proof. Whenever, then, two or more alternate proofs of validity are possible for an argument, choose that which is the most elegant. If all possible proofs are equally elegant, the choice is an arbitrary one.

Let us give an example of an argument in English for which two different proofs of validity, each involving a different number of statements, are possible. The argument follows:

EXAMPLE   45

> If Arthur is going to propose marriage to Grace, then he must buy her a ring. If he must buy her a ring, his bank account will dwindle. Arthur either is going to propose marriage to Grace or he is going to join the Navy. If Arthur is going to join the Navy, he can save some money. If he can save some money, he will set up his own business. Hence, either Arthur's bank account will dwindle or he will set up his own business. (PM, BR, AD, JN, SM, OB)

The longer, and hence less elegant, proof for the validity of this argument follows:

EXAMPLE   46

<u>∠ ∴ AD V OB</u>

1. PM ⊃ BR	Premise
2. BR ⊃ AD	Premise
3. PM V JN	Premise
4. JN ⊃ SM	Premise
5. SM ⊃ OB	Premise
6. PM ⊃ AD	From 1, 2, and A_3
7. JN ⊃ OB	From 4, 5, and A_3
8. ∴ AD V OB	From 6, 7, 3, and A_6

The shorter, more elegant proof follows:

EXAMPLE   47

<u>∠ ∴ AD V OB</u>

1. PM ⊃ BR	Premise
2. BR ⊃ AD	Premise
3. PM V JN	Premise
4. JN ⊃ SM	Premise
5. SM ⊃ OB	Premise
6. BR V SM	From 1, 4, 3, and A_6
7. ∴ AD V OB	From 2, 5, 6, and A_6

Although both proofs are equally correct, the second one is prefer-able on the grounds of elegance.

Exercises

The addition of A_6 to your repertoire of valid argument forms will allow you to construct proofs for the validity of the following arguments. Use the suggested notation.

176. If Darwin is not wrong, animals evolved along one line. If Bergson is right, animals evolved along divergent lines. Darwin is not wrong or else Bergson is right. Therefore animals evolved along one line, or they evolved along divergent lines.   (DW, OL, BR, DL)

177. If Aristotle was right, the highest good is happiness. If Plotinus was right, the highest good is reunion with the One. Either Aristotle or Plotinus was right. Therefore either the highest good is reunion with the One or it is happiness.   (AR, GH, PR, RO)

178. Bach's keyboard works sound well on the clavichord or on the harpsi-

chord. If Bach's keyboard works sound well on the harpsichord, they should be played on the harpsichord. If Bach's keyboard works sound well on the clavichord, they should be played on the clavichord. Therefore Bach's keyboard works should be played on the harpsichord or they should be played on the clavichord. (SC, SH, PH, PC)

179. Jane has pneumonia or congestion caused by excess smoking. If Jane has pneumonia, then Jane has a fever. If Jane has a fever, then she needs medical treatment. If she has congestion caused by excess smoking, she should give up cigarettes, at least temporarily. Jane does not need medical treatment. Therefore Jane should give up cigarettes, at least temporarily. (JP, JC, HF, NT, GC)

180. Grace will pack a box lunch if she is sure Arthur will invite her to the picnic. Either she is sure that Arthur will invite her to the picnic, or she is going to check with Jane. If she is going to check with Jane, she is making a big mistake. Grace is not making a big mistake. Hence she will pack a box lunch. (BL, SA, CJ, BM)

181. This tree is deciduous or I am mistaken. If I don't know botany I should learn it. If this tree is deciduous, it will lose its leaves in the winter. If I am unfamiliar with this particular species of tree, I should acquaint myself with it. This tree won't lose its leaves in the winter. If I am mistaken, then I don't know botany or I am unfamiliar with this particular species of tree. Therefore I should learn botany or I should acquaint myself with this particular species of tree. (TD, M, KB, LB, LL, US, A)

182. If John told Grace the truth, then Arthur seriously wants to marry her. If Arthur seriously wants to marry Grace, he will stop dating Jane. John told Grace the truth, or else he is trying to win favor with Jane. If John is trying to win favor with Jane, then he doesn't want Arthur to invite Jane to the picnic. If John doesn't want Arthur to invite Jane to the picnic, then he may tell Grace that Arthur is fickle. Accordingly, either Arthur will stop dating Jane, or John may tell Grace that Arthur is fickle. (TT, MG, SD, WF, AI, AF)

183. Newton's ethereal theory is correct, or else either the Cartesian vortex theory is incorrect or Leibniz's theory of the conservation of energy is correct. If Newton's objections to the Cartesian vortex theory are valid, then his positive theory of planetary motions is correct. If Newton's ethereal theory is not correct, then if Leibniz's theory of the conservation of energy is correct we don't need a Newtonian ether to renew motion. If the Cartesian vortex theory is incorrect, then Newton's objections to it are valid. Newton's ethereal theory is not correct. Hence we don't need a Newtonian ether to renew motion, or Newton's positive theory of planetary motions is correct. (NT, CV, LC, OV, PM, ER)

184. If Arthur considers all alternatives, then he will think carefully about pro-

posing marriage to Grace only if he is not going to join the Navy. Arthur considers all alternatives if he is not foolish. If Arthur can't make snap decisions, then he is foolish if he acts hastily. If Arthur considers the future important, then he acts hastily or he will think carefully about proposing marriage. Arthur is foolish or he considers his future important. Arthur can't make snap decisions if he considers his future important. Arthur is not foolish. Consequently Arthur is not going to join the Navy.   (CA, TC, JN, F, SD, AH, FI)

185. If John is concerned about Jane's cough, he is going to ask Grace to persuade Jane to see a physician. If he is going to ask Grace to persuade Jane to see a physician, Grace will be alarmed. John is concerned about Jane's cough, or he realizes she smokes too much. If he realizes that Jane smokes too much, he is going to try to persuade her to give up cigarettes. If he is going to try to persuade her to give up cigarettes, she will not go to the picnic with him. Grace will not be alarmed. Hence Jane will not go to the picnic with John.   (JC, AG, GA, RS, GC, GP)

§13.   Simplification, Conjunction, and the Commutativity of Conjunction

In addition to statements of the forms $P \supset Q$, $\sim P$, and $P \vee Q$, there are frequently encountered in ordinary language, and hence also in the language of logic, statements of the form "P and Q". Examples of this are numerous. We look out of the window, for example, and remark, "It is raining, *and* the sun is shining." Or we enter a basement room and exclaim, "This room is damp *and* it's cold, too." Since such statements are used constantly in arguments ordinarily encountered in everyday discourse, we shall, if our logic is to encompass them, have to introduce a symbol to represent the conjunction "and". The symbol which we shall use is the *dot* (·). Thus, instead of "P and Q", we write $P \cdot Q$.

Just as we discovered earlier that the form "if · · · then—", had several variants in ordinary language, although all were representable by · · · ⊃ —; so we find several variants, in ordinary language, of "· · · and —", all representable by the form · · · · —. Some of these variants follow:

EXAMPLE   48

a. It is raining and the sun is shining.

   b. It is raining but the sun is shining.
   c. It is raining although the sun is shining.
   d. It is raining even though the sun is shining.
   e. It is raining, nevertheless the sun is shining.
   f. It is raining, yet the sun is shining.
   g. It is raining, still the sun is shining.
   h. It is raining; moreover the sun is shining.
   i. It is raining; in addition the sun is shining.
   j. It is raining; as well, the sun is shining.
   k. It is raining; further the sun is shining.
   l. It is raining; furthermore the sun is shining.
  m. It is raining, whereas the sun is shining.
   n. It is raining; however, the sun is shining.
   o. It is raining, albeit the sun is shining.
   p. It is raining; also the sun is shining.
   q. It is raining, but so is the sun shining.
   r. It is raining, but also the sun is shining.
   s. It is raining despite the fact that the sun is shining.
   t. It is raining in spite of the fact that the sun is shining.
   u. It is raining regardless of the fact that the sun is shining.
   v. It is raining at the same time that the sun is shining.
  w. It is raining, while the sun is shining.
   x. Not only is it raining, but also the sun is shining.
   y. Not only is it raining, but the sun is shining as well.
   z. Not only is it raining, but further the sun is shining.

If we take R as a translation of "It is raining", and S as a translation of "The sun is shining", then all of the statements of Example 48 may be symbolically translated simply by R · S. Some of these statements differ in *emotive* significance, yet they are all logically identical. They all represent the fact that two statements, designated by R and S, are simultaneously assertable. Some of them stress the fact that it is unusual for S to be assertable when R is assertable, and draw attention to this unusual situation by employing words like "but also" or "nevertheless" in place of "and", which is fairly neutral in *emotive* significance and is incapable of stressing any one fact more than another.

In a logical argument, if we are given a conjunction of the form $P · Q$, we very often wish to use just one of the conjuncts. Thus, for example, if "It is raining and the sun is shining" is a true statement, we may wish to conclude that "It is raining" is, by itself, a true statement; and we may wish to conclude that "The sun is shining" is also, taken by itself, a true statement. We must, therefore, introduce two new valid argument forms which will enable us to conclude, from any given conjunction, that either conjunct is by itself true. The first of these forms, known as "the *principle of simplification*", is represented symbolically as follows:

A_7: $P \cdot Q$
$\therefore P$

A_7 allows us to extract the first member of a conjunction. But suppose we wish to extract the second member. This is no problem, for since conjunction is obviously a commutative operation, if we introduce another valid argument form asserting the commutativity of conjunction, we can then, by the new form and A_7, conclude Q from $P \cdot Q$. The new form, called "the principle of the commutativity of conjunction", is stated symbolically as follows:

A_8: $P \cdot Q$
$\therefore Q \cdot P$

Let us see how we would use these two forms to prove the validity of the following argument: "It is raining and the sun is shining. Hence, the sun is shining." If the two atomic statements of this argument are represented by R and S, respectively, then our proof of validity will be as follows:

$$\angle \therefore S$$

1. R $\cdot$ S   Premise
2. S $\cdot$ R   From 1, and A_8
3. $\therefore$ S   From 2, and A_7

Recall that when we introduced the principle of the commutativity of the inclusive disjunction (A_5), we noted that instead we could have introduced the following form:

$$P \lor Q$$
$$\sim Q$$
$$\therefore P$$

So here, instead of A_8, we could have introduced the following:

$$P \cdot Q$$
$$\therefore Q$$

But we have already seen that A_5 is useful in more cases than the alternate form suggested (for example, when the conclusion of an argument of form A_6 is of the form $Q \lor P$, and we desire a conclusion of the form $P \lor Q$). So here we choose to introduce A_8 rather than the alternate form because of its greater utility.

Perhaps it has occurred to the reader that a principle which is the opposite of the principle of simplification could also be introduced into our logic, namely, the principle that if two statements are true singly, then the conjunction of them will also be true. There is, in fact, such a principle in logic, known as "the *principle of conjunction*". It is formalized in the following valid argument form, which we shall call "A_9":

A_9: P
Q
$\therefore P \cdot Q$

The utility of the three new valid argument forms (A_7, A_8, and A_9) will be evident in the following group of exercises.

Exercises

The addition of these three valid argument forms to the ones previously learned will enable you to construct a proof for the validity of each of the following arguments. Use the suggested notation.

186. If I hurry, I will catch the bus; and I'll hurry. Therefore I will hurry and catch the bus.   (H, CB)
187. Arthur is late and Grace is angry. Therefore Grace is angry and Arthur is late.   (AL, GA)
188. If it rains, Jane will stay home. Jane will not stay home. Hence it will not rain and Jane will not stay home.   (R, SH)
189. If we accept traditional harmony, a fifth is a concord and a second is a dissonance. We accept traditional harmony. Therefore a fifth is a concord.   (AH, FC, SD)
190. Jane will either stay home or go shopping. Jane will not stay home, and if she goes shopping she will have lunch with John. Therefore Jane will have lunch with John, and she will not stay home.   (SH, GS, HL)
191. Salaries remain constant. If prices go up, the cost of living will rise. The cost of living will not rise. If salaries remain constant, and prices don't go up; then living conditions will not change. Therefore living conditions will not change.   (SC, PU, CR, LC)

192. Arthur arrived late and Grace chided him; moreover Arthur said he was sorry and Grace forgave him. Therefore Arthur said he was sorry although Grace chided him, but Grace forgave him despite the fact that he arrived late. (AL, GC, AS, GF)

193. If we accept the Schönbergian system, then every note is of equal importance and there is no one tonal center. We shall accept the Schönbergian system. Traditional harmony is limiting. Therefore there is no one tonal center, and traditional harmony is limiting. (AS, EI, TC, HL)

194. If there is free will and responsibility, then there is choice and men are not machines. There is free will and there are ethical standards. Ethical standards imply responsibility. Men are moral beings. Therefore men are not machines but are moral beings. (FW, R, C, MM, ES, MB)

195. Either I study hard or I fail the test. I will not fail the test. I'll fail the test if I fail to finish it in fifty minutes. Either I submit a completed examination paper or I fail to finish the test in fifty minutes. Therefore I study hard and I submit a completed examination paper. (SH, FT, FF, CE)

§14. Abbreviated Proofs of Validity

Once the proper method of constructing proofs of validity for arguments is understood, the construction of future proofs may be greatly facilitated by an abbreviated method of proof. The principle involved in abbreviated proofs is this: any proof may be condensed, *as long as complete reasons are given for all statements in the proof.* Let us illustrate with the proof for the validity of the following argument in English:

EXAMPLE 49

Grace is going to give Arthur a new pipe; and if she gives him a new pipe, he will be pleased. Therefore he will be pleased. (NP, P)

Formerly, we would have constructed the proof for the validity of this argument as follows:

EXAMPLE 50

$\angle \therefore P$

1. $NP \cdot (NP \supset P)$ Premise
2. $(NP \supset P) \cdot NP$ From 1, and A_8
3. $NP \supset P$ From 2, and A_7

  4. NP   From 1, and A_7
  5. $\therefore$ P   From 3, 4, and A_1

Now, however, we can construct an abbreviated proof for the validity of this argument in the following manner:

EXAMPLE   51

$$\underline{\qquad\diagup \therefore P \qquad}$$

  1. NP $\cdot$ (NP $\supset$ P)   Premise
  2. NP $\supset$ P   From 1, A_8; and A_7
  3. $\therefore$ P   From 2; 1, A_7; and A_1

Nothing has actually been omitted in this proof of validity; all the necessary reasons are given. The reason given for statement 2 indicates that we have applied A_7 to what we got from statement 1 and A_8. Hence A_8 is mentioned first (for that is the form first used); and the semicolon in the reason indicates that A_7 (mentioned after the semicolon) is applied to what is mentioned before the semicolon, namely, what was obtained from statement 1 and A_8. Likewise, the reason given for statement 3 indicates that A_1 is applied to statement 2 and the statement obtained from statement 1 and A_7. Here, statement 2 is the first statement required by the final application of A_1, so statement 2 is mentioned first. Since what we got from statement 1 and A_7 is the statement required by the second premise of our form A_1, we mentioned "1, A_7" second. Each of the two parts required by the premises of the form A_1 is set off by a semicolon.

Even less writing need be involved in the construction of a proof of validity if we adopt these conventions: Abbreviate "Premise" by "Pr.", and omit the words "from" and "and". Then the abbreviated proof of the validity of the above argument will finally appear as follows:

EXAMPLE   52

$$\underline{\qquad\diagup \therefore P \qquad}$$

  1. NP $\cdot$ (NP $\supset$ P)   Pr.
  2. NP $\supset$ P   1, A_8; A_7
  3. $\therefore$ P   2; 1, A_7; A_1

Abbreviated proofs should be used with discretion. If it is easier in some cases to write out all the statements involved, then do not abbreviate just for the sake of abbreviation. On the other hand, when it is perfectly evident what statements are involved, and it seems a waste of time to write them all out, then abbreviate. However, *make it a cardinal rule, when constructing abbreviated proofs of validity, always to give complete reasons, with their component parts in the proper order.* The following reason for statement 2 of Example 52 would be incorrect because the order is wrong: "1, A_7; A_8".

§15. The Principle of Double Negation

The next two valid argument forms which we shall introduce illustrate what logicians call "the *principle of double negation*". These are:

A_{10}: P $\qquad\qquad$ A_{11}: $\sim \sim P$
$\qquad$ $\therefore \sim \sim P$ $\qquad\qquad\qquad$ $\therefore P$

The following argument in English illustrates why these two new forms are necessary:

EXAMPLE 53

I won't stay home, only if it isn't raining. It is raining. Hence I will stay home.   (SH, R)

Let us begin our proof of the validity of this argument:

$\diagup \ \therefore$ SH

1. $\sim$SH $\supset$ $\sim$R   Pr.
2. R   Pr.

Though A_2 will obviously be used in proving the validity of this argument, we cannot use A_2 directly, for A_2 requires that its second premise negate the consequent of the first premise. Also the conclusion of A_2 is the negation of the antecedent of the first premise. Furthermore, both of these negations are indicated in A_2 by means of the tilde. There is, however, no tilde in the second premise or in the conclusion of the argument of Example 53. What we need, in order to use A_2, is shown by the following diagram:

EXAMPLE   54

Form Used: A_2

$\sim$SH	$\supset$	$\sim$R
P	$\supset$	Q

$\sim$	$\sim$R
$\sim$	Q

$\therefore$	$\sim$	$\sim$SH
$\therefore$	$\sim$	P

Our guiding principle here must be uniform replacement. Since Q is replaced by $\sim$R in the first premise of A_2, Q must be replaced by $\sim$R in the second premise as well. Since Q appears in the second premise in the molecular statement form $\sim Q$ and since Q is replaced by $\sim$R, $\sim Q$ will accordingly be replaced by $\sim \sim$R, as our diagram indicates. This needed $\sim \sim$R can be got from the second premise of our argument by A_{10}.

Likewise, since P is replaced by $\sim$SH in the first premise, P will be replaced in the conclusion by $\sim$SH. Since P appears in the conclusion in the molecular statement form $\sim P$, and since P is replaced by $\sim$SH, $\sim P$ will accordingly be replaced by $\sim \sim$SH, as the diagram of Example 54 indicates. The desired conclusion, SH, can then be got from $\sim \sim$SH by A_{11}.

We are now able to complete our proof of the validity of the argument of Example 53:

$\diagup \quad \therefore$ SH

1. $\sim$SH $\supset$ $\sim$R   Pr.
2. R   Pr.
3. $\sim \sim$R   2, A_{10}
4. $\sim \sim$SH   1, 3, A_2
5. $\therefore$ SH   4, A_{11}

Let us look at one more argument in English, whose proof of validity involves a *triple* negation:

EXAMPLE 55

If Arthur is going to get a new job on Monday, then it is not true that he won't have enough money to buy Grace a birthday present. Arthur won't have enough money to buy Grace a birthday present. Therefore he isn't going to get a new job on Monday.   (NJ, BP)

The proof of the validity of this argument follows:

EXAMPLE 56

$$/ \therefore \sim NJ$$

1. NJ $\supset$ $\sim$ $\sim$BP   Pr.
2. $\sim$BP   Pr.
3. $\sim$ $\sim$ $\sim$BP   2, A_{10}
4. $\therefore$ $\sim$NJ   1, 3, A_2

The following diagram shows why the triple negation is necessary in this proof of validity:

EXAMPLE 57

Form Used: A_2

NJ	$\supset$	$\sim$ $\sim$BP
P	$\supset$	Q

$\sim$	$\sim$ $\sim$BP
$\sim$	Q

$\therefore$	$\sim$	NJ
$\therefore$	$\sim$	P

Since $\sim \sim$BP is taken as the instance of Q in the first premise of A_2, it will also have to be taken as the instance of Q in the second premise. Accordingly $\sim Q$ will have to be replaced by $\sim \sim \sim$BP, as the diagram indicates. The required $\sim \sim \sim$BP is got from $\sim$BP (statement 2 of our argument) by means of A_{10}, as shown below:

EXAMPLE   58

Form Used: A_{10}

$\sim$BP
P

$\therefore$	$\sim$	$\sim$	$\sim$BP
$\therefore$	$\sim$	$\sim$	P

Here $\sim$BP is uniformly taken as the instance of P in the premise and in the conclusion of A_{10}.

Four or more negation signs can be similarly treated, although they will rarely be encountered.

Exercises

Using all the valid argument forms now at your disposal, construct a proof of validity for each of the following arguments, using the suggested notation. If you find the abbreviated method of proof convenient, use it.

196. If Jane is going to give Grace a birthday party, then it isn't true that she's not thoughtful. Jane is not thoughtful. Accordingly, she is not going to give Grace a birthday party.   (BP, T)

197. If Arthur isn't going to take Grace to dinner on her birthday, she is not going to enjoy the occasion. Grace is going to enjoy the occasion. Hence Arthur is going to take Grace to dinner on her birthday.   (TG, EO)

198. If it doesn't rain tomorrow, the sun will shine. The sun will not shine. Either it doesn't rain tomorrow or the weatherman is unreliable. There-

fore it is not the case that the weatherman is not unreliable. (RT, SS, WU)

199. It will not rain tomorrow or the sun will not shine. It will rain tomorrow. It will be cold and it is not the case that the pavements will not be slippery. Therefore the sun will not shine and the pavements will be slippery. (RT, SS, C, PS)

200. Diamonds are hard, whereas copper is soft. If diamonds are hard, they can cut lead. If copper is soft, then it is not the case that it cannot be cut by a diamond. Therefore copper can be cut by a diamond, and it is not the case that diamonds cannot cut lead. (DH, CS, CL, CD)

201. The idea of God is innate, or else either the idea of God comes from experience or Locke is not correct on this point. The idea of God is innate only if Cartesian theology is not in error; but Cartesian theology is in error while Locke is correct on this point. Hence the idea of God comes from experience. (I, E, L, C)

202. If earthquakes are destructive, they should be prevented if science possesses the appropriate means of prevention. Either it is not the case that earthquakes are not destructive, or it is not the case that they are not useful. Earthquakes are not useful. Therefore they should be prevented if science possesses the appropriate means of prevention. (D, P, S, U)

203. If the dog has a license tag, he will not be picked up by the dogcatcher. If he is on a leash, he has a responsible owner. The dog is on a leash or he has a license tag. If the dog either will not be picked up by the dogcatcher or has a responsible owner, then he is not a stray dog. Therefore he is not a stray dog. (LT, DC, OL, RO, SD)

204. If John has poor grades, then he can try to bring them up if he cares enough; but if he's not serious about his school work, then he won't bother to raise his grades if he prefers social life to homework. It is not the case both that he has poor grades and isn't serious about his school work, only if it's not the case that he either cares enough or prefers social life. He cares enough or he prefers social life to homework. Therefore he either can try or he won't bother to raise his grades. (PG, T, C, SW, B, SL)

205. The good man is not discontented. If the life of reason is valuable, men will pursue it; but if men are irrational, they will seek pleasure. If it is not the case that either Bentham or Plato is right, then the good man is discontented. If Bentham is right, then this means that men are irrational; whereas if Plato is right, it follows that the life of reason is valuable. Therefore men will pursue the life of reason or they will seek pleasure. (GD, RV, MP, MI, SP, BR, PR)

§16. The Principle of Addition

Our twelfth valid argument form is called "the *principle of addition*", and is formulated as follows:

A_{12}: P
∴ $P \lor Q$

The principle needs very little explanation. It states that if any statement is true, then the inclusive disjunction of that statement and any second statement is also true. That this form is valid is evident from a consideration of the fact that for an inclusive disjunctive statement to be true, at least one of its disjuncts must be true, and possibly both may be true. The premise of our new argument form asserts the truth of the first disjunct of the conclusion, and hence it does not matter whether the second disjunct is true or false. In either case, the conclusion of an argument of the form A_{12} will be true if its premise is true.

A simple instance of this argument form in English will help to illustrate its validity: "Grace will go shopping. Hence, Grace will go shopping or she will meet Arthur." It does not matter whether or not Grace actually does meet Arthur; the conclusion of this argument will still be true because the premise tells us that she is at least going shopping.

Suppose we wish to prove the validity of an argument of this form:

$$P$$
$$\therefore Q \lor P$$

What we would do is conclude $P \lor Q$ from P by the principle of addition, and then commute this to $Q \lor P$ by A_5.

EXERCISES

Construct a proof of validity for each of the following arguments, using the suggested notation. You may use the abbreviated method of proof.

206. **Man** is the measure of all things. Therefore man is the measure of all things or Protagoras was wrong.   (MM, PW)
207. The good life is desirable. Hence either Aristotle was wrong or the good life is desirable.   (LD, AW)
208. If Aristotle was right, then the good life is desirable. Aristotle was right.

Hence either the good life is desirable or Aristotle was not right.   (AR, LD)

209. Aristotle was correct. If either Aristotle was correct or Plato was correct, then the good life is desirable. Hence the good life is desirable.   (AC, PC, LD)

210. There is a World of Ideas or Plato was wrong. Hence either there is a World of Ideas or Plato was wrong, or else Aristotle was right.   (WI, PW, AR)

211. There is a World of Ideas. Thus, Aristotle was right, or else either there is a World of Ideas or Plato was wrong.   (WI, AR, PW)

212. There is a World of Ideas or Plato was wrong. Hence Aristotle was right, or else either Plato was wrong or there is a World of Ideas.   (WI, PW, AR)

213. If the good life is desirable, then Aristotle was right or Plato was right. That the ethical theories of the ancient Greek philosophers are significant is a necessary condition for the fact that either Plato was right or Aristotle was right. The good life is desirable. Hence Plato was right or the ethical theories of the ancient Greek philosophers are significant. (LD, AR, PR, TS)

214. If Plato was not right, then Aristotle's judgment of his predecessors is justified. If Socrates was a great philosopher then Aristotle's judgment of his predecessors is not justified. Socrates was a great philosopher or his reputation is due entirely to Plato's apotheosis of him, even though Plato was not right. Accordingly, Socrates' reputation is due entirely to Plato's apotheosis of him or Aristotle's judgment of his predecessors is not justified; moreover, Plato was right or Socrates was not a great philosopher.   (P, A, S, R)

215. The reputation accorded Plato by tradition is justified if Plato was correct; and the reputation accorded Socrates by tradition is justified if Socrates was correct. Either Socrates was correct or Plato was correct. Hence it is the case that either the reputation accorded Plato by tradition is justified or the reputation accorded Socrates by tradition is justified; or else it is not the case that either the reputation accorded Socrates by tradition is justified or the reputation accorded Plato by tradition is justified.   (RP, PC, RS, SC)

CHAPTER THREE

Definitions

§17. Definition of $P \lor Q$

The statement forms which we have thus far been using as models for the translation of statements of ordinary language are the following:

    1. P
    2. $P \cdot Q$
    3. $P \lor Q$
    4. $P \supset Q$
    5. $\sim P$

Note that the logical symbols used, other than the Roman letters representing statements, are the following (which are known as "logical operators", or simply as "operators"): $\cdot$, $\lor$, $\supset$, and $\sim$. Some of the functions represented by these operators can be expressed in terms of fewer of these symbols. For example, of these operators, $\cdot$ and $\sim$ will suffice to express all statements which have hitherto been expressed by the use of $\lor$ and $\supset$. In other words, the operators $\cdot$ and $\sim$ constitute what is known as "*a functionally complete set* of operators" for the types of statements thus far employed in our logic. That these two operators constitute a functionally complete set is indicated by writing them enclosed in braces and separated by a comma, thus: $\{\,\cdot\,,\,\sim\,\}$.

The qualification that $\{\,\cdot\,,\,\sim\,\}$ is functionally complete *for the types of statements thus far employed in our logic* must be made, for we shall see later that different types of statements require that this set, which we are provisionally calling our "functionally complete set", be expanded.

Further, even for statements of the types thus far considered, there are other functionally complete sets besides $\{\cdot, \sim\}$. The sets $\{\sim, \vee\}$ and $\{\sim, \supset\}$ are each functionally complete. Thus, if we take $\{\cdot, \sim\}$ as our functionally complete set, we can define $\vee$ and $\supset$ in terms of these two operators. Or, if $\{\sim, \vee\}$ is taken as the functionally complete set, $\cdot$ and $\supset$ can be defined in terms of these operators. Again, if $\{\sim, \supset\}$ is taken as functionally complete, these two operators will serve to define $\cdot$ and $\vee$.

All that is meant by functional completeness is that, with just the operators of the functionally complete set *and with the aid of no other operators,* any logical statement may be expressed. Given a functionally complete set of operators, the other operators are introduced *by definition,* i.e., they are defined in terms of the operators which constitute the functionally complete set.

Definitions in symbolic logic have practical as well as theoretical advantages. The main practical advantage is that of any definition, namely, it enables one to replace a long and sometimes cumbersome expression by a shorter, more convenient one. Thus, as in English, we introduce the short expression, "square", by definition, to replace the longer expression, "plane figure of four equal sides having four right angles"; so in symbolic logic we can introduce a single operator to express the same thing that a certain combination of other operators would express.

A second practical advantage of definitions in symbolic logic is that they help us to see novel implications of statements in the English language which might otherwise have escaped us. Thus we shall see what a disjunctive statement of the inclusive type means in terms of conjunction and negation; and we shall also see what hypothetical conditional statements mean in terms of conjunction and negation.

The main theoretical advantage of definitions in symbolic logic is that they reduce the number of operators which must be assumed as primitive, since the other operators can be introduced by definition. Thus, definitions help to enhance the elegance of a logical system.

Let us adopt the set $\{\cdot, \sim\}$ as the one in terms of which we shall express our other operators, and show how the others may be expressed in terms of this set. First of all, let us show how $P \vee Q$ can be defined in terms of $\{\cdot, \sim\}$. In our definitions, we shall use the sign for *definitional equivalence,* namely $=_{df}$, which may be read as "equals by definition", or "is defined as", or "is definitionally equivalent to". The definition of $P \vee Q$ in terms of $\{ \cdot, \sim \}$, which we shall call *"Definition I"*, follows:

Definition I: $P \vee Q =_{df} \sim(\sim P \cdot \sim Q)$

In other words, $P \vee Q$ means that it is not the case that neither P nor Q is true. For example, "It is raining or the sun is shining" means "It is not the case both that it is not raining and that the sun is not shining."

What the inclusive disjunction means is that at least one of the disjuncts must be true, and possibly both of them are true. The case that is excluded is that in which both are false. And this is exactly what Definition I states, namely that the disjuncts cannot both be false.

Let us give an argument in English, and show how Definition I would be needed in proving its validity. "Definition I", in our reasons, will be abbreviated as "D_I".

EXAMPLE   59

It is not the case both that motion is not measurable and that time is not measurable. Motion is not measurable or bodies do not move in space. Bodies move in space if they are extended. Bodies are extended. Hence it follows that time is measurable.   (MM, TM, BM, BE)

The proof of the validity of this argument follows:

EXAMPLE   60

/ ∴ TM

1.	$\sim(\sim MM \cdot \sim TM)$	Pr.
2.	$\sim MM \vee \sim BM$	Pr.
3.	$BE \supset BM$	Pr.
4.	BE	Pr.
5.	BM	$3, 4, A_1$
6.	$\sim \sim BM$	$5, A_{10}$
7.	$\sim BM \vee \sim MM$	$2, A_5$
8.	$\sim MM$	$7, 6, A_4$
9.	$MM \vee TM$	$1, D_I$
10.	$\therefore TM$	$9, 8, A_4$

In this proof, we employed Definition I by going from an *un-*

abbreviated form (in statement 1) to the *abbreviated* form using the wedge (in statement 9). One can as well proceed from the *abbreviated* form to the *unabbreviated*, as in the proof of the validity of the following argument:

EXAMPLE 61

> Arthur will invite Jane to the dance or he will invite Grace. Hence it is not the case both that Arthur will not invite Jane to the dance and that he won't invite Grace.   (IJ, IG)

Here is the proof of the validity of this argument:

EXAMPLE   62

$$\diagup \therefore \sim(\sim IJ \cdot \sim IG)$$

1. IJ ∨ IG   Pr.
2. ∴ ∼(∼IJ · ∼IG)   1, D_I

Exercises

Employing Definition I, in addition to the valid argument forms which you know, construct a proof for the validity of each of the following arguments. Use the suggested notation.

216. If John won't continue dating Jane and won't date Myra, then he is plagued with indecision. John is not plagued with indecision. Hence either he will continue dating Jane or he will date Myra.   (CD, DM, PI)

217. It is not the case both that there is not a World of Ideas and that Plato is not wrong. There is not a World of Ideas. If Plato is wrong, then the theory of Ideas is useless. Hence it is not true that the following is not the case; namely, both that the theory of Ideas is useless and that there is not a World of Ideas.   (WI, PW, TU)

218. It is not the case both that this exercise is not easy and that it is not difficult. This exercise is not difficult or you are not having trouble with it. You are having trouble with it if you are poorly prepared. You are poorly prepared. Hence this exercise is easy.   (E, D, T, P)

219. If Jane and John go to the bridge party, they will meet Myra. If John is cordial to Myra, Jane will be jealous. It is not the case both that Jane and John won't go to the bridge party and that John won't be cordial to Myra. Hence they will meet Myra or Jane will be jealous.   (BP, MM, JC, JJ)

220. Aristotle was not wrong. If man is a rational animal, then either he is responsible for his ethical acts or he is responsible for his motives. Aristotle

was wrong or man is a rational animal. Therefore it is not the case both that man is not responsible for his ethical acts and that he is not responsible for his motives.   (AW, MR, EA, RM)

221. If Grace and Arthur go to the bridge party, they will meet Jane and John. It is not the case both that they will not go to the bridge party and that they will not go to the movies. If they go to the movies, they will have a good time. Hence it is not the case both that they will not meet Jane and John and that they will not have a good time.   (BP, JJ, M, GT)

222. It is not the case both that Grace and Arthur will not go to the bridge party and that they will not go to a movie. If they go to the bridge party, they will meet John and Jane. If Arthur won't do as Grace asks, they won't meet John and Jane. Arthur won't do as Grace asks, although he wants her to have a good time. Hence Arthur wants Grace to have a good time, and they will go to a movie.   (BP, M, JJ, GA, GT)

223. If Jane isn't really fond of John and doesn't associate with him just to make Arthur jealous, then her motives are not clear. Even though John has not questioned Jane, he is understandably confused if her motives are not clear. It is not the case both that it isn't true that John is not understandably confused and that he has not questioned Jane. Thus Jane is really fond of John or she associates with him just to make Arthur jealous.   (FJ, MJ, MC, QJ, UC)

224. There is an internal sense of beauty and deformity, or Hutcheson was wrong. If Hutcheson was wrong, then it is not the case both that Hume's modifications of Hutchesonian theory are not correct and that Hume did not also err. If Hume was in fact his own best critic; then if Hume's modifications of Hutchesonian theory are correct, mankind universally agrees in matters of taste. It is not true that Hume was not his own best critic, and furthermore there is not an internal sense of beauty and deformity. If Hume also erred, then aesthetics admits of relativism. Hence it is not the case both that mankind does not universally agree in matters of taste and that aesthetics does not admit of relativism.   (IS, HW, MC, HE, BC, AT, AR)

225. If motion is the measure of time, then if motion is irregular, time is irregular. Motion is the measure of time. If we can measure motion, then if motion is regular, time is regular. If our scientists are to be trusted, then it is not the case both that motion is not irregular and that motion is not regular. If common sense is right, we can measure motion; and if science is valid, then our scientists are to be trusted. Common sense is right, and science is valid. Therefore it is not the case both that time is not irregular and that time is not regular.   (MT, MI, TI, MM, MR, TR, ST, CR, SV)

§18.   Definition of $P \supset Q$

Just as we defined the inclusive disjunction in terms of our functionally complete set of operators $\{\, \cdot,\, \sim \,\}$, so we can define the hypothetical conditional in terms of this set. This new definition, which we shall call *"Definition II"*, follows:

Definition II: $P \supset Q =_{df} \sim(P \cdot \sim Q)$

Let us explain this definition. $P \supset Q$ means that it is not the case that P can be true at the same time that Q is false. For example, "If I drop X, it will fall" means "It is not the case both that I drop X and X will not fall."

We can also explain Definition II in terms of necessary conditions. $P \supset Q$ implies that, since Q is a necessary condition for P, it will never happen that we will have P and not have the condition which is necessary for P. And this is exactly what is stated by Definition II.

Definitions I and II suggest that, since both the inclusive disjunction and the hypothetical conditional can be defined in terms of conjunction and negation, it ought to be possible to transform hypothetical conditional statements into inclusive disjunctive statements, and vice versa. And, in fact, this is quite possible. For example, given the inclusive disjunctive statement: "Either Arthur will invite Jane to the dance or she will go with John", which we shall symbolize as IJ ∨ GJ; let us prove that the hypothetical conditional statement: "If Arthur will not invite Jane to the dance, then she will go with John", symbolized as $\sim$IJ $\supset$ GJ, can be derived from it. The proof follows:

EXAMPLE   63

$$/ \therefore \sim\text{IJ} \supset \text{GJ}$$

1. IJ ∨ GJ	Pr.
2. $\sim(\sim\text{IJ} \cdot \sim\text{GJ})$	1, D_I
3. $\therefore \sim\text{IJ} \supset \text{GJ}$	2, D_{II}

In this proof of validity, we have used the symbol, D_{II}, as the abbreviation for "Definition II". This convention will be followed in designating all future definitions in our proofs.

Let us show, by means of diagrams, exactly how statements 2 and 3 of our proof were obtained.

EXAMPLE   64

To Get Statement 2:

Using Definition I

Statement 1:

IJ	V	GJ
P	V	Q

~	(	~	IJ	·	~	GJ	)
~	(	~	P	·	~	Q	)

EXAMPLE   65

To Get Statement 3:

Using Definition II

Statement 2:

~	(	~IJ	·	~	GJ	)
~	(	P	·	~	Q	)

~IJ	⊃	GJ
P	⊃	Q

Conversely, to get from a hypothetical conditional to an inclusive disjunction, the reverse procedure is followed. Thus, if we are given the statement: "If Arthur will not invite Jane to the dance, then she will go with John," we can conclude "Either Arthur will invite Jane to the dance or she will go with John." Using the same notation as before, we prove this inference valid thus:

EXAMPLE   66

$$/ \therefore IJ \lor GJ$$

1. ~IJ ⊃ GJ   Pr.
2. ~(~IJ · ~GJ)   1, D$_{II}$
3. ∴ IJ ∨ GJ   2, D$_I$

Diagrams will again explain this:

EXAMPLE   67

To Get Statement 2:

Using Definition II

Statement 1:

~IJ	⊃	GJ
P	⊃	Q

~	(	~IJ	·	~	GJ	)
~	(	P	·	~	Q	)

EXAMPLE   68

To Get Statement 3:

Using Definition I

Statement 2:

~	(	~	IJ	·	~	GJ	)
~	(	~	P	·	~	Q	)

IJ	∨	GJ
P	∨	Q

When using Definition II (as well as the other formal definitions which we shall introduce into our logic) in a proof of validity for an argument, we can, as we did with Definition I, proceed either from the *unabbreviated* form to the *abbreviated* form (as was done in Example 63), or from the *abbreviated* form to the *unabbreviated* form (as was done in Example 66).

The transformation of ∨ statements to ⊃ statements, and vice versa, illustrates the practical advantage of definition in that novel implications which hold among statements come to light when definitions are employed.

EXERCISES

Construct a proof of the validity of each of the following arguments, using the suggested notation:

226. If it is not going to rain, then I will go down town. Hence either it is going to rain or I will go down town. (R, DT)
227. This object is red. Therefore if this object is not red, then it is some other color. (OR, OC)
228. It is not the case both that a substance is radioactive and not dangerous; and it is not the case both that a substance is dangerous and one should not avoid it. Hence it is not the case both that a substance is radioactive and one should not avoid it. (R, D, A)
229. If Arthur asks Grace to marry him and she does not accept, then Jane will be pleased. Jane will not be pleased. Therefore, if Arthur asks Grace to marry him, she will accept. (AG, GA, JP)
230. If Grace doesn't accept and Arthur isn't disappointed, then Jane will not be amazed. Jane will be amazed. Hence Arthur will be disappointed if Grace doesn't accept. (GA, AD, JA)
231. The following is not the case; namely, that John will ask Myra to marry him and she will not accept, and also that Jane will not be pleased. Jane will not be pleased. Therefore Myra will accept if John will ask her to marry him. (AM, MA, JP)
232. If John doesn't tire of Jane, he will ask Jane to marry him. If John does tire of Jane, he will ask Myra to marry him. If John asks Jane to marry him, Myra will be disappointed. Hence if John doesn't ask Myra to marry him, Myra will be disappointed. (TJ, AJ, AM, MD)
233. It is not the case both that the soul is mortal and will not cease to exist at the death of the body; and it is not the case both that the soul is not im-

mortal and not mortal. It is not the case both that the soul is immortal and will not survive the death of the body. Therefore it is not the case both that the soul will not cease to exist at the death of the body and that the soul will not survive the body's death.   (SM, CE, SI, SD)

234. It is not the case both that the sun goes around the earth and that Venus does not go around the earth; and it is not the case both that the sun does not go around the earth and that the earth does not go around the sun. It is not the case both that Venus goes around the earth and that it will not be eclipsed by the earth. It is not the case that Venus will be eclipsed by the earth. Therefore the earth goes around the sun.   (SE, VE, ES, EE)

235. If it is not the case both that Arthur asks Grace to marry him and she doesn't refuse, then John will ask Jane. John will not ask Jane to marry him. If Grace's mother attempts to interfere and Grace does not persuade her that they should get married, then Arthur won't ask Grace to marry him. If Jane isn't truthful to Grace about Arthur, although Grace's mother doesn't attempt to interfere, then Grace will refuse to marry Arthur. If Jane is truthful to Grace and does not try to interfere, then John will ask Jane to marry him. Hence if Jane doesn't attempt to interfere, Grace will persuade her mother that she and Arthur should get married.   (AG, GR, JJ, MI, GP, JT, JI)

§19.   The Biconditional

By definition, we can introduce another useful logical operator, known as "the *triple bar*", namely, $\equiv$, which has not been used heretofore. By $P \equiv Q$ we shall mean $(P \supset Q) \cdot (Q \supset P)$. This is not yet a definition of the triple bar in terms of $\{ \cdot, \sim \}$, of course. We shall give such a definition presently, after we have explained more precisely what we intend by the triple bar.

Instead of going through the circumlocution of saying that P implies Q, and Q implies P, we shall write $P \equiv Q$, which is read "P if, and only if, Q". Remember that $P \supset Q$ was a translation of "P only if Q" and of "Q if P". Now, if the implication works both ways, so that P and Q mutually imply one another, i.e., such that $(P \supset Q) \cdot (Q \supset P)$, it is much simpler to say merely "P if, and only if, Q", and write $P \equiv Q$ to express the fact that the implication normally represented by $\supset$ here works both ways. Since the implication does work both ways, we call statements of the form $P \equiv Q$ "*biconditionals*". From what has been said concerning the biconditional, it is evident that, in addition to "*P* if, and only if, *Q*", other variants translated by $P \equiv Q$ are these: "*P* is a necessary and sufficient condition for *Q*", and "*P* is logically equivalent to *Q*".

Let us illustrate the significance of the biconditional by an example from ordinary language. A painter may wish to assert that if a certain paint is red, then it is not some other color. He may further wish to assert that if the paint is not some other color, then it is red. If we represent "This paint is red" by PR, and "This paint is some other color" by OC, then we can represent, symbolically, his two statements as follows:

1. PR $\supset$ ~OC
2. ~OC $\supset$ PR

By A_9, we can combine the two statements as follows:

3. (PR $\supset$ ~OC) $\cdot$ (~OC $\supset$ PR)

By applying our knowledge of the biconditional, we see that the painter is asserting that his paint is red if, and only if, it is not some other color. This same fact can be expressed by saying "That this paint is red is a necessary and sufficient condition for it not being some other color", or by saying "The fact of this paint being red is logically equivalent to the fact of its not being some other color." All of these expressions may be represented by PR $\equiv$ ~OC.

We are now ready to give a completely unabbreviated definition of the biconditional in terms of $\{\ \cdot,\ \sim \}$. Thus far we have merely described $P \equiv Q$ as meaning $(P \supset Q) \cdot (Q \supset P)$. But since we already know (by Definition II) how to write $P \supset Q$ using only $\cdot$ and $\sim$, we can easily write $(P \supset Q) \cdot (Q \supset P)$ in terms of $\cdot$ and $\sim$, thus: $\sim(P \cdot \sim Q) \cdot \sim(Q \cdot \sim P)$. Since this is what is meant by $P \equiv Q$, we have arrived at our formal definition of the triple bar in terms of $\{\ \cdot,\ \sim \}$. We shall call this definition "*Definition III*".

Definition III: $P \equiv Q =_{df} \sim(P \cdot \sim Q) \cdot \sim(Q \cdot \sim P)$

Continuing with our example of the painter, let us offer a proof of the validity of the following argument, which he might have proposed:

EXAMPLE 69

> If this paint is red, then it is not some other color. If this paint is not some other color, then it is red. Therefore this paint is red if, and only if, it is not some other color. (PR, OC)

We would prove the validity of this argument in the following manner:

EXAMPLE 70

$$\diagdown \therefore PR \equiv \sim OC$$

1.	$PR \supset \sim OC$	Pr.
2.	$\sim OC \supset PR$	Pr.
3.	$\sim(PR \cdot \sim \sim OC)$	1, D_{II}
4.	$\sim(\sim OC \cdot \sim PR)$	2, D_{II}
5.	$\sim(PR \cdot \sim \sim OC) \cdot \sim(\sim OC \cdot \sim PR)$	3, 4, A_9
6.	$\therefore P \equiv \sim OC$	5, D_{III}

Because the biconditional is defined formally in terms of $\{ \cdot, \sim \}$, and not in terms of the hypothetical conditional, we could not, in the proof above, just combine statements 1 and 2 by A_9, and then go to the conclusion, giving as our reason "D_{III}".

An abbreviated proof of the validity of the argument of Example 69 is, of course, possible. It would appear thus:

EXAMPLE 71

$$\diagdown \therefore PR \equiv \sim OC$$

1.	$PR \supset \sim OC$	Pr.
2.	$\sim OC \supset PR$	Pr.
3.	$\therefore PR \equiv \sim OC$	1, D_{II}; 2, D_{II}; A_9; D_{III}

EXERCISES

Construct a proof of validity for each of the following arguments, using the suggested notation:

236. Arthur will join the Navy if, and only if, Grace does not marry him. Arthur will not join the Navy. So it isn't true that it is not the case both that Grace marries Arthur and that he will not join the Navy. (JN, GM)

237. Grace will marry Arthur if, and only if, he asks her. Either Arthur goes into the Navy or he asks Grace to marry him. Hence either Arthur goes into the Navy or Grace will marry him. (GM, A, AN)

238. That Locke's theory of ideas is not wrong is a necessary and sufficient condition for the fact that ideas are not innate; moreover, the idea of God comes from experience if, and only if, ideas are not innate. Hence Locke's theory of ideas is wrong or the idea of God comes from experience.   (TW, II, GE)

239. John will not marry Jane if, and only if, he prefers Myra. John will marry Jane if, and only if, Myra fails to prevent it. If he prefers Myra, he will marry her. Hence if Myra doesn't fail to prevent John from marrying Jane, then he will marry Myra.   (MJ, PM, MF, MM)

240. The utilitarian proof that the good is desirable is not fallacious if, and only if, Mill was not in error. The objections to the proof are not well-founded if, and only if, Mill was not in error. Hence the utilitarian proof that the good is desirable is fallacious, or the objections to it are not well-founded. (PF, ME, OF)

241. $2 + 2 = 4$ is a necessary truth only if it is capable of being established a priori; and if it is capable of being established a priori, then it is a necessary truth. $2 + 2 = 4$ is capable of being established a priori if, and only if, it is an analytic statement. Hence $2 + 2 = 4$ is a necessary truth if, and only if, it is an analytic statement.   (NT, CE, AS)

242. If the legislature passes the new housing bill, our war veterans will have better living accommodations; and they will in fact have better living accommodations only if the legislature passes the bill. They will have better living accommodations if, and only if, pressure is brought to bear on the legislature. Hence it is not the case both that pressure will be brought to bear on the legislature and that they will not pass the bill.   (PB, BA, PL)

243. Men are not rational animals if, and only if, Aristotle's analysis of human nature is not correct. Aristotle's analysis of human nature is correct if, and only if, his ethical system is valuable in practice. Men are rational animals. Hence if Aristotle's ethical system is not valuable in practice, then his psychology has merely historical interest.   (MR, AC, SV, HI)

244. The soul is mortal if, and only if, it is not immortal. The soul is immortal if, and only if, it survives the death of the body. It is not the case both that the soul is mortal and does not cease to exist at the death of the body. Hence it cannot be the case both that the soul does not survive the death of the body and that it does not cease to exist at the death of the body. (SM, SI, SD, CE)

245. Spinach builds muscles if, and only if, it contains large quantities of protein. Cartoon fans have been deceived if spinach doesn't build muscles. While spinach doesn't contain large quantities of protein, it is nevertheless true that green and leafy vegetables are recommended for a balanced diet. Thus cartoon fans have been deceived, even though green and leafy vegetables are recommended for a balanced diet.   (BM, CP, FD, VR)

§20.   The Exclusive Disjunction

As we mentioned earlier, there are two distinct senses of the English word "or", which are referred to as the *"inclusive"* and *"exclusive"* senses. Thus far we have been concerned with disjunctive statements of the *inclusive* type only. We said that in the *inclusive* disjunction, represented by the wedge, V, at least one of the disjuncts must be true, and perhaps both of them may be true. In the *exclusive* disjunction, *exactly* one (in other words, not both) of the disjuncts is true. If one is true, the other is false. The following two statements illustrate the distinction between the two senses of "or":

EXAMPLE 72

> a. Either Clara Andrews or John Andrews is home, for I see a light burning in their house.
> b. Either John Andrews is home or he is not home.

In a, we evidently do not wish to mean that Clara and John cannot both be home at the same time. This then is an *inclusive* disjunction. We might have been more precise and said "Clara and/or John is/are home." But this is stilted, even though unambiguous.

In b, however, which is an *exclusive* disjunction, it is plain that John can't both be home and not home at the same time. We might have made this more precise (but again more stilted) by saying "John is home or he is not home, but not both."

Though in ordinary discourse we do not make these fine distinctions, they are obviously significant for purposes of logical analysis, especially where the validity of arguments is concerned. If your host at a dinner party asks you if you want mashed or French fried potatoes, he does not want "Yes" as an answer, because he is thinking in terms of the *exclusive,* rather than the *inclusive,* sense of "or". Rarely are these two senses of "or" distinguished in English by use of a phrase like "and/or" to designate the *inclusive* disjunction, and "either · · · or—but not both" to indicate the *exclusive* disjunction. The sense in English is generally judged by context. Often in English, however, it is not clear which sense is meant.

Thus, although English generally uses one word, "or", ambiguously to designate both the inclusive and the exclusive disjunction, logic can quite easily distinguish them by using a different symbol for each. Having already used the wedge, V, to indicate the *inclusive* disjunction, let us use the *circled wedge,* Ⓥ, to indicate the *exclusive* disjunction. Then the statement "Clara Andrews is home or John Andrews is home" will be translated by CH V JH; while the statement "John Andrews is home or he is not home" will be translated by JH Ⓥ ~JH.

Let us now see if we can establish a definition, in terms of our functionally complete set of operators, of the exclusive disjunction. Just what do we mean to assert by the exclusive disjunction? It would seem that we mean $P \vee Q$ plus the additional qualification $\sim(P \cdot Q)$. In other words, we want to add to what is meant by the inclusive disjunction the qualification that not both members of the disjunction can be true. Hence by P Ⓥ Q we mean $(P \vee Q) \cdot \sim(P \cdot Q)$. But this is not a completely unabbreviated definition of P Ⓥ Q in terms of $\{ \cdot, \sim \}$. However, if we substitute the unabbreviated form of $P \vee Q$ in the expression $(P \vee Q) \cdot \sim(P \cdot Q)$, we arrive at the following:

Definition IV: $\quad P$ Ⓥ $Q =_{\text{df}} \sim(\sim\text{P} \cdot \sim\text{Q}) \cdot \sim(\text{P} \cdot \text{Q})$

If John is at home or at his office, presuming, of course, that his office is not located in his home, this means that he is not at neither place (or, in other words, that he is at least at one place), and further that he is not at both places. That he is not at neither place may be represented by $\sim(\sim\text{H} \cdot \sim\text{O})$, and that he is not at both places may be represented by $\sim(\text{H} \cdot \text{O})$. Putting these two expressions together, we arrive at $\sim(\sim\text{H} \cdot \sim\text{O}) \cdot \sim(\text{H} \cdot \text{O})$, which, by Definition IV, is equivalent to H Ⓥ O. And this is what we intended by the statement that John is at home or at his office.

EXERCISES

GROUP A

246. Construct five English statements unambiguously utilizing the *inclusive* disjunction.
247. Construct five English statements unambiguously utilizing the *exclusive* disjunction.

GROUP B

For each statement of Group B, decide whether it unambiguously utilizes the *inclusive* disjunction, or unambiguously utilizes the *exclusive* disjunction, or is ambiguous. If it is ambiguous, state what conditions would need to be known to decide whether the inclusive or the exclusive disjunction is intended.

248. He will be home tonight, or he may prefer that I see him at another time.
249. Men consider the problem of space illogically or they consider it rationally.
250. Modern science is right, or ancient science is right.
251. Men are mortal or Aristotle was wrong.
252. You can buy Scotch tape at the dime store or at the drug store.
253. Space is Euclidean or space is non-Euclidean.
254. I would like to study French or German this semester.
255. Spinach builds muscles or else it is not high in protein content.
256. Either causal inferences are justifiable, or experience cannot validate causality.
257. Men believe in innate ideas or they reject the doctrine of innate ideas.
258. John will marry Jane or he will marry Myra.
259. Arthur will marry Grace or he will join the Navy.
260. Arthur will join the Navy or he will not join the Navy.

GROUP C

Construct a proof of validity for each of the arguments in Group C, using the suggested notation:

261. Men believe in innate ideas or they are Lockeans, but not both. If men believe in innate ideas, they are fools; but men are not fools. Therefore men are Lockeans. (B, L, F)
262. Right is derived from good. Either good is the same as beauty or they are different (but not both). Good is not the same as beauty. Hence good and beauty are different, and it is not the case that right is not derived from good. (RD, GS, D)
263. The idea of solidity originates either in reflection or in sensation, but not both. The following is not the case; namely, both that the idea of solidity originates in sensation and that it is not the case that it does not originate in reflection. Hence that the idea of solidity does not originate in reflection is a necessary and sufficient condition for it originating in sensation. (R, S)
264. It is a known fact that cancer is always fatal, or else some patients recover from cancer (but not both). It is not the case that it is a known fact that cancer is always fatal; and in fact if some patients recover from cancer, then its early discovery may be significant. Therefore it is not the case that the early discovery of cancer may not be significant. (KF, PR, DS)
265. If men first exist in a state of "all against all," then a social contract is necessary. If men are created in a peaceful state, there is always tranquillity. Either men first exist in a state of "all against all," or they are

created in a peaceful state (but not both). There is not always tranquillity. Therefore a social contract is necessary.   (SA, SC, PS, AT)

266. It is not the case both that the moral sentiment is a calm passion and that Hume is not right; and indeed the moral sentiment is a calm passion. If Hume is right, passions are not the slave of reason. Either passions are the slave of reason, or reason is the slave of the passions (but not both). Therefore reason is the slave of the passions.   (SP, HR, PS, RP)

267. If Easter is the first Sunday after the first full moon after the vernal equinox, then astronomers can easily calculate its date. Easter in fact falls either on some other Sunday or on the first Sunday after the first full moon after the vernal equinox, but not both. Hence Easter falls on some other Sunday and/or it is easy for astronomers to calculate its date.   (FS, EC, OS)

268. If I don't like this new LP recording of the *Hammerklavier Sonata,* then I'll keep my old 78 r.p.m. set. A necessary and sufficient condition for me to like this new LP recording is that it is a superb performance. A necessary and sufficient condition for me to keep my old 78 r.p.m. set is that I prefer it to the new LP version. It is not the case both that the new recording is a superb performance and that I prefer the old version. Therefore either the new recording is a superb performance or I prefer the old version, but not both.   (LR, OS, SP, P)

269. A necessary condition for reason to be the slave of the passions is that it can only recommend qualities to the moral sentiment for approval; whereas that reason can only recommend qualities to the moral sentiment for approval is a sufficient condition for the fact that reason cannot be the basis of moral distinctions. Reason is the slave of the passions; and further either sentiment is the basis of moral distinctions or reason is the basis of moral distinctions (but not both). Therefore sentiment is the basis of moral distinctions.   (RS, RQ, RB, SB)

270. Men consider the problem of space illogically or they consider it rationally, but not both. Euclid's geometry is the only conceivable geometry only if alternative geometries are inconceivable. That modern science is right is a sufficient condition for the fact that if space is relative, then spatial calculations may be relational. If men consider the problem of space rationally, then objects exist in absolute space if space is absolute. If Euclid's geometry is not the only conceivable geometry, then either space is absolute or space is relative (but not both). Men do not consider the problem of space illogically. It is not the case both that modern science is not right and that ancient science is not right. Alternative geometries are not inconceivable, even though ancient science is not right. Therefore it is not the case both that objects do not exist in absolute space and that spatial calculations may not be relational.   (CI, CR, EC, AI, MR, SR, SC, OE, SA, AR)

CHAPTER FOUR

Truth Tables and Their Implications

§21.   Truth Tables for Negation and Conjunction

Truth and falsity are properties of statements, not of arguments. Arguments are valid or invalid, sound or unsound; but the individual statements (whether premises or conclusions) which constitute the arguments are true or false. Consider the following argument:

EXAMPLE 73

> Spinach builds muscles only if it contains large quantities of protein. Spinach does not contain large quantities of protein. Consequently spinach does not build muscles.   (BM, CP)

This argument is valid, as we can easily prove:

EXAMPLE 74

$$\diagup \therefore \sim\text{BM}$$

1. BM ⊃ CP   Pr.
2. ∼CP   Pr.
3. ∴ ∼BM   1, 2, A_2

The individual statements constituting the argument (represented, respectively, by BM ⊃ CP, ∼CP, and ∼BM) are each either true or false. As a matter of fact, each of them is true, and not false; and hence the argument we say is not only valid but *sound*. For, as we recall, in a valid argument, *if* its premises are true, the conclusion *will be* true; whereas a sound argument is a valid one in which the premises *are in fact true,* and in which, consequently, the conclusion *is in fact true.*

In ordinary discourse, we are concerned not only with the validity or invalidity of an argument, but also with the truth or falsity of its constituent statements. Thus, while it is necessary to know whether an argument is valid or invalid, we do not stop there. We want to know if, further, it is *sound;* that is to say, we want to know whether the statements constituting the argument are true or false. Reflection on the following example will make this evident:

EXAMPLE 75

If spinach is high in protein content, then it builds muscles. Spinach is high in protein content. Hence spinach builds muscles.

This argument is, of course, valid, as we can easily prove by A_1. But, plainly, if we were to present this argument to our next door neighbor, who does not happen to like spinach, he would be convinced that there is something queer about logic if it can be used to prove such an obviously false conclusion as that spinach builds muscles. Yet we never claim to have proved that the conclusion is true, but only that the argument is valid. Still, our next door neighbor is not contented with this answer. He wants to know if spinach builds muscles. The question then is this: *"In a valid argument, what exactly is the relation of the truth value of the conclusion to the truth values of the premises?"* (In the formulation of this question, we use the term "truth value" to designate the property of being true or false.)

The easiest way to tackle this problem is to introduce what the logician calls "truth tables".

In a two-valued logic, any statement may be either true or false. There is no third possibility. Let us take the statement that spinach is high in protein content. We represent the fact that this statement (which we shall represent symbolically by P), and in fact *any* statement, is either true or false, by means of the following truth table, in which the value "true" is designated by T, and the value "false" by F.

Truth Table for Any Statement

P
T
F

This is elementary enough, and represents the simplest type of truth table. With regard to our example, it means that the statement "Spinach is high in protein content" is either true or false. (Need we add, "but not both"?)

Suppose, however, that we are considering two statements, of which one is the negation of the other. For instance, let P represent the positive statement, "Spinach is high in protein content"; and let $\sim P$ represent the negative statement "Spinach is not high in protein content." What is the relation of the truth values of these two statements? It takes no great reflection to realize that P is true if, and only if, $\sim P$ is false; and that $\sim P$ is true if, and only if, P is false. In other words, to use our example, "Spinach is high in protein content" is true if, and only if, "Spinach is not high in protein content" is false; and vice versa. We can represent this relation in the following manner:

Truth Table for Any Statement and Its Negation

P	$\sim P$
T	F
F	T

This truth table indicates all the possible combinations of truth values of P and $\sim P$. In a given case, such as that in which P represents "Spinach is high in protein content" and is *false,* we can see, as our truth table reveals, that its negation $\sim P,$ representing "Spinach is not high in protein content", is *true.*

At this point, we have established the truth table for one of the two operators in our functionally complete set, namely $\sim$ in the set, $\{\cdot, \sim\}$. We are now ready to formulate a rule concerning the relation of the truth value of any statement to that of its negation:

Rule 1: The negation of a statement has a truth value which is the reverse of that of the original statement.

Let us see if we can establish a truth table for $\cdot$, the other operator of our functionally complete set. If we can do this, then we shall be able to discourse on the truth or falsity of any statement which our logic, so far as we have developed it, is equipped to handle; for any statement of the forms thus far considered can be expressed in terms of $\{ \cdot, \sim \}$.

Now if we are to establish a truth table for statements of the form $P \cdot Q$, i.e., for any molecular statement which is conjunction of two statements (whether atomic or molecular), we must first establish the possible combinations of the truth values of the two statements separately considered (i.e., when not in conjunction). Continuing our example, we shall take P to represent "Spinach is high in protein content", and Q to represent "Spinach builds muscles." A little reflection will reveal that there are four possible combinations of the truth values of these, or of *any* two statements, whether atomic or molecular. P can be true when Q is true or when Q is false, and P can be false when Q is true or when Q is false. This we represent in the following manner:

Truth Table for Two Statements

P	Q
T	T
T	F
F	T
F	F

It is the fourth row (horizontally) of this truth table which represents the case with regard to our example of spinach and its muscle-building virtues. For both "Spinach is high in protein content" and "Spinach builds muscles" are false.

Using this information concerning the possible relations of the truth and falsity of any two statements, let us construct a truth table which will exhibit the further relation of the possible truth values of any molecular statement of the form $P \cdot Q$, to the possible truth values of its two constituents, P and Q. The following truth table is the one which will result:

Truth Table for the Conjunction of Two Statements

P	Q	$P \cdot Q$
T	T	T
T	F	F
F	T	F
F	F	F

The first two columns, which represent the standard relations of the truth values of P and Q, are called "reference columns". The reference columns will always be separated from the other columns by a double vertical line, as in the truth table above.

Since the fourth row (horizontally) of this truth table again represents the case of our statements about spinach, we see that since "Spinach is high in protein content" is false, and since "Spinach builds muscles" is also false, it follows that the resultant conjunction of these two statements, "Spinach is high in protein content, and spinach builds muscles", is also false. And this is just what we should expect of a conjunction, namely, that it could not possibly be true if each of its conjuncts is false. In fact, the only case in which we should expect a conjunction to be true is that in which each of its conjuncts is true. As our truth table shows, this case (represented by the first row) is the only one in which a conjunction is true. As we should also expect, and as our truth table indicates, if one of the conjuncts is true and the other false (rows 2 and 3), or if both are false (row 4), then the resultant conjunction is false.

Accordingly, we may formulate the following rule concerning the relation of the truth value of a conjunction to the truth values of its conjuncts:

Rule 2: A conjunction is true if, and only if, each of its conjuncts is true; otherwise it is false.

EXERCISE

271. Illustrate, with sentences of the English language, the four (horizontal) rows of the truth table for conjunction. Select your sentences so that the

actual truth and falsity of their atomic constituents corresponds exactly to the various possible cases of the truth table.

§22.   Truth Tables for Statements of the Forms, P ∨ Q, P ⊃ Q, P ≡ Q, and P Ⓥ Q

Since we have defined ∨, ⊃, ≡, and Ⓥ, in terms of our functionally complete set of operators, $\{\cdot, \sim\}$, and since we have established truth tables for the two operators · and ∼ in our functionally complete set, we can determine truth tables for ∨, ⊃, ≡, and Ⓥ, by establishing truth tables for their definitions in terms of $\{\cdot, \sim\}$. Once we have done this, we shall be able, if we know the truth value of *P* and of *Q* in any given case, to ascertain what will be the truth value of *P* ∨ *Q*, or of *P* ⊃ *Q*, or of *P* ≡ *Q*, or of *P* Ⓥ *Q*, depending on the molecular statement under consideration.

Let us proceed to the construction of a truth table for *P* ∨ *Q*. We have already learned that *P* ∨ *Q* is defined as ∼(∼*P* · ∼*Q*). Now, since we know the truth tables for · and ∼, we can easily establish one for ∼(∼*P* · ∼*Q*), which is the definition of *P* ∨ *Q*. This we do as follows:

P	*Q*	∼*P*	∼*Q*	∼*P* · ∼*Q*	∼(∼*P* · ∼*Q*)
T	T	F	F	F	T
T	F	F	T	F	T
F	T	T	F	F	T
F	F	T	T	T	F

Let us explain this. The first two vertical columns are our familiar reference columns for *P* and *Q*. They merely state the various possible combinations of truth and falsity of any two statements. Column 3 is the opposite of the first column (inasmuch as ∼*P* is the negation of *P*), and column 4 is the opposite of the second column (inasmuch as ∼*Q* is the negation of *Q*). Now, since we have previously established that a conjunction is true if, and only if, each of its conjuncts is true, let us examine the conjunction of column 5, viz., $\sim P \cdot \sim Q$. In the first (horizontal) row of our truth table, we see that $\sim P$ is false and $\sim Q$ is false. Therefore, in row 1, $\sim P \cdot \sim Q$ is false. In row 2, we again see that not both of the conjuncts are true, and so we must again put an F in column 5. The same is true of the third row. Only in row 4 do we find that $\sim P$ and $\sim Q$ are both true, and that, accordingly, $\sim P \cdot \sim Q$ is true. Finally, column 6 is the opposite of column 5. The truth table of column 6 is our truth table for the disjunction $P \vee Q$, since it is the truth table for the definition of $P \vee Q$.

The final column of our truth table is exactly what we should expect for the inclusive disjunction. This column indicates that both disjuncts can be true and the disjunction will be true (row 1), and that the disjunction will still be true if only one disjunct is true (rows 2 and 3). If both disjuncts are false, then the disjunction is false (row 4).

Now that we have established the truth table for $P \vee Q$ by using the truth tables which we already knew for conjunction and negation, we can state the truth table for $P \vee Q$ simply as follows:

Truth Table for Inclusive Disjunction

P	Q	$P \vee Q$
T	T	T
T	F	T
F	T	T
F	F	F

On the basis of this true table, let us formulate a rule concerning the truth values of inclusive disjunctive statements:

Rule 3: The inclusive disjunction is true if at least one of its disjuncts is true, and false otherwise.

EXERCISES

272. Construct English statements to illustrate all the cases of the truth table for inclusive disjunction. Be sure the actual truth values of your English statements correspond to those of the various cases of the truth table.

273. In the same manner that we constructed a truth table for $P \vee Q$ by using the truth tables for negation and conjunction, construct a truth table for the hypothetical conditional $P \supset Q$ in terms of its definition.

274. Construct English statements to illustrate all the cases of the truth table for the hypothetical conditional. Be sure the actual truth values of your English statements correspond to the various cases of the truth table.

275. On the basis of your truth table for the hypothetical conditional, formulate Rule 4, concerning the truth values of hypothetical conditional statements, in terms of the truth values of their antecedents and consequents.

276. Construct a truth table for the biconditional $P \equiv Q$ in terms of its definition, using the truth tables for negation and conjunction.

277. Construct English statements to illustrate all the cases of the truth table for the biconditional. Be sure the actual truth values of your English statements correspond to the various cases of the truth table.

278. On the basis of your truth table for the biconditional, formulate Rule 5, concerning the truth values of biconditional statements, in relation to their constituents.

279. Construct a truth table for the exclusive disjunction, $P \circledtext{V} Q$, in terms of its definition, using the truth tables for negation and conjunction.

280. Construct English statements to illustrate all the cases of the truth table for the exclusive disjunction. Be sure the actual truth values of your English statements correspond to the various cases of the truth table.

281. On the basis of your truth table for the exclusive disjunction, formulate Rule 6, concerning the truth values of exclusive disjunctions, in terms of the truth values of their disjuncts.

§23.   Abbreviated Truth Tables

Just as there is an abbreviated method of proving the validity of an argument, so there is a way of constructing abbreviated truth tables. And, just as with the abbreviated proofs, the principle which we followed was that nothing should be omitted from our reason for any statement, so here we shall find that nothing is omitted from the abbreviated truth tables.

To construct a truth table for any statement, we had previously constructed a separate column to represent each component of the statement. In an abbreviated truth table, we merely write our column of truth values under that part of the statement to which the column applies. Let us illustrate this by constructing an abbreviated truth table for the definition of the inclusive disjunction, $\sim(\sim P \cdot \sim Q)$. First, we shall need our columns for P and Q, which we shall write directly under P and Q, thus:

$\sim$	($\sim$	P	$\cdot$	$\sim$	Q)
		T			T
		T			F
		F			T
		F			F

Next, we need columns for $\sim P$ and $\sim Q$. These we shall add to our table in this manner: under the tilde before the P, we shall write the column for $\sim P$; and under the tilde before the Q, we shall write the column for $\sim Q$, thus:

$\sim$	($\sim$	P	$\cdot$	$\sim$	Q)
	F	T		F	T
	F	T		T	F
	T	F		F	T
	T	F		T	F

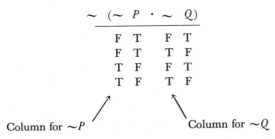

Column for $\sim P$ Column for $\sim Q$

Now we need a column for the conjunction of $\sim P$ and $\sim Q$. This we shall write under the dot which indicates the conjunction of $\sim P$ and $\sim Q$, thus:

$\sim$	($\sim$	P	$\cdot$	$\sim$	Q)
	F	T	F	F	T
	F	T	F	T	F
	T	F	F	F	T
	T	F	T	T	F
*			↑	*	

Column for conjunction of the
two statements whose truth columns are marked with asterisks

Finally, we need a column for the negation of this conjunction, which shall be written under the first tilde:

~	(~	P	·	~	Q)
T	F	T	F	F	T
T	F	T	F	T	F
T	T	F	F	F	T
F	T	F	T	T	F
			*		

↑

Column for the negation of the
statement whose column is
marked with an asterisk

This is our completed truth table. The final column constructed
(marked with the arrow) represents the possible truth values of
$\sim(\sim P \cdot \sim Q)$, when P and Q have the values stated.

Exercises

282. Construct an abbreviated truth table for the definition of the hypothetical conditional.
283. Construct an abbreviated truth table for the definition of the biconditional.
284. Construct an abbreviated truth table for the definition of the exclusive disjunction.

§24. Proving Validity and Invalidity by Truth Tables

For every deductive argument there corresponds a hypothetical
conditional statement whose antecedent is the premise or conjunction of premises of the argument, and whose consequent is the conclusion of the argument. For any deductive argument, in other words,
there corresponds a statement of the form "*if* premises, *then* conclusion". Hence to construct the "if · · · then—" statement corresponding to a deductive argument, we insert a horseshoe between the
premise (or conjunction of premises) and the conclusion. If the argument has one premise, its corresponding hypothetical conditional
statement will be of the form $P \supset C$, where P stands for "premise"
and C stands for "conclusion". If the argument contains two premises, which we shall designate by P^1 and P^2, its corresponding hypo-

thetical conditional statement will be of the form $(P^1 \cdot P^2) \supset C$, in which the two premises are conjoined by the sign for conjunction $\cdot$. How are we to treat a conjunction of three or more premises when we consider them collectively as constituting the antecedent of an "if $\cdots$ then—" statement? Since we have considered a conjunction to have only two members, a conjunction of three premises (P^1, P^2, and P^3) will be considered as a conjunction of the following type:

$$(P^1 \cdot P^2) \cdot P^3$$

In similar fashion, we can treat a whole host of premises as *one* conjunction. For example, if we have five premises, we can consider them as a conjunction of the following type:

$$\{[(P^1 \cdot P^2) \cdot P^3] \cdot P^4\} \cdot P^5$$

A valid deductive argument is one whose premise or premise set always implies its conclusion, no matter what the truth values of the atomic statements concerned. Accordingly a valid deductive argument is one whose corresponding hypothetical conditional statement is always true. Let us construct a truth table for the statement form which corresponds to A_1 (*modus ponens*), to illustrate this:

Unabbreviated Truth Table

P	Q	$P \supset Q$	$(P \supset Q) \cdot P$	$[(P \supset Q) \cdot P] \supset Q$
T	T	T	T	T
T	F	F	F	T
F	T	T	F	T
F	F	T	F	T

This can also be represented in abbreviated form, as follows:

Abbreviated Truth Table

$[(P$	$\supset$	$Q)$	$\cdot$	$P]$	$\supset$	Q
T	T	T	T		T	
T	F	F	F		T	
F	T	T	F		T	
F	T	F	F		T	

Since the statement form which corresponds to A_1 is always true, we may conclude that A_1 is a valid argument form. It is valid for any argument whatsoever which is an instance of it, regardless of the truth values of the individual statements involved. Only row 1 (horizontally) of the truth table for A_1, however, represents the case of a *sound* argument, namely, that in which the premises *are in fact true,* and in which, consequently, the conclusion is true. The other three rows represent cases of valid, but *unsound,* arguments.

A statement which is always true is called "a tautology", or "an analytic statement". We see then that a deductive argument is valid if, and only if, its corresponding hypothetical conditional statement is a tautology. Thus, we may now redefine the term "valid deductive argument" as follows:

A valid deductive argument is one whose corresponding hypothetical conditional statement is a tautology.

An invalid argument, on the other hand, is one whose corresponding hypothetical conditional statement is not always true. For example, let us consider the fallacy of affirming the consequent, which, we recall, is the following form:

$$P \supset Q$$
$$Q$$
$$\therefore P$$

The hypothetical conditional statement form corresponding to the fallacy of affirming the consequent is $[(P \supset Q) \cdot Q] \supset P$. Its truth table follows:

Unabbreviated Truth Table

P	Q	$P \supset Q$	$(P \supset Q) \cdot Q$	$[(P \supset Q) \cdot Q] \supset P$
T	T	T	T	T
T	F	F	F	T
F	T	T	T	F ⟵
F	F	T	F	T

Or again, let us use the abbreviated form of the truth table to represent the same thing:

Abbreviated Truth Table

$$[(P \supset Q) \cdot Q] \supset P$$

T	T	T	T	T
T	F	F	F	T
F	T	T	T	F ←
F	T	F	F	T

Since there is an instance, marked with an arrow in both truth tables, where this statement form is false, it therefore corresponds to an *invalid* argument form.

A statement such that the final column of its truth table contains at least one T and at least one F is called "a contingent statement" or "a synthetic statement"; and a statement such that the final column of its truth table contains all F's and no T's is called "a contradiction" or "a contradictory statement". Now, since the hypothetical conditional statement corresponding to an invalid deductive argument has at least one F in the final column of its truth table, we may offer the following definition of "invalid deductive argument":

An invalid deductive argument is one whose corresponding hypothetical conditional statement is either a contingent statement or a contradictory statement.

The hypothetical conditional statement form corresponding to the fallacy of affirming the consequent was contingent, since the final column of its truth table contained at least one T. But consider the argument form,

$$\sim(P \cdot \sim P)$$
$$\therefore P \cdot \sim P$$

The final column for the truth table for its corresponding hypothetical conditional statement form contains no T's, and is therefore contradictory. The argument form, accordingly, is invalid. For the corresponding hypothetical conditional statement form of this argument form we give, this time, just the abbreviated truth table:

$$[\sim(P \cdot \sim P)] \supset (P \cdot \sim P)$$

T	T F F		F		F
T	F F T		F		F

↑

Incidentally, since this argument form involves only one variable, the truth table for its corresponding hypothetical conditional statement form contains only two rows (horizontally).

EXERCISES

GROUP A

285. How can we define "valid deductive argument" in terms of "tautology"?
286. How can we define "invalid deductive argument" in terms of "contingent statement" and "contradictory statement"?
287. What is an analytic statement?
288. What is the relationship between a tautology and a contradiction?
289. What is a contingent statement?
290. What is a synthetic statement?

GROUP B

Prove, by the use of abbreviated truth tables, that the following argument forms are valid. Apply Rules 1 to 6 for the construction of truth tables, rather than construct a truth table for the definition of each statement form.

291. A_2	296. A_9
292. A_4	297. A_{10}
293. A_5	298. A_{11}
294. A_7	299. A_{12}
295. A_8	

GROUP C

Prove, by the use of the abbreviated truth table method, that the following argument forms are invalid:

300. The Fallacy of Denying the Antecedent.
301. $P \vee P$
    $\therefore \sim P$
302. $P \vee \sim P$
    $\therefore \sim (P \vee \sim P)$

303. $P \vee Q$
    P
    $\therefore \sim Q$
304. $P \vee Q$
    Q
    $\therefore \sim P$

GROUP D

Decide, by the use of abbreviated truth tables, whether the following arguments are valid or invalid. Use the suggested notation.

305. Men are mortal. Therefore men are mortal and/or gods are divine. (MM, GD)

306. If the temperature of water is lowered to 32° F., the water will freeze. If the temperature of water is not lowered to 32° F., then the water will not freeze. Therefore water will freeze if, and only if, its temperature is lowered to 32° F.   (TL, WF)

307. It is not the case both that diamonds are hard and lead is hard. Therefore diamonds are not hard and lead is not hard.   (DH, LH)

308. It is not the case both that students study hard and fail examinations. Therefore students don't study hard and/or they don't fail examinations. (SH, FE)

309. The soul is immortal or the soul is mortal, but not both. Hence the soul is mortal, and/or the soul is immortal.   (SI, SM)

310. Water freezes at 32° F. Hence, if I lower the temperature of this water to 32° F., it will freeze at that temperature.   (WF, LT)

311. Men are mortal and/or gods are divine. Men are mortal. Therefore gods are not divine.   (MM, GD)

312. The soul is mortal or the soul is immortal, but not both. The soul is immortal. Therefore the soul is not mortal.   (SM, SI)

313. If it's raining, I'm taking an umbrella. Hence, if I'm not taking an umbrella, it's not raining.   (R, U)

314. Myra will marry John if, and only if, he asks her. Hence the following is not the case; namely, that either Myra will marry John or he asks her (but not both).   (MM, A)

315. Jane will either go shopping or she will visit Myra, but not both. Hence the following is not the case; namely, that Jane will go shopping if, and only if, she visits Myra.   (GS, VM)

316. Jane will either go shopping or she will visit Myra, but not both. Hence Jane will not visit Myra if she goes shopping.   (GS, VM)

317. All men are mortal or Aristotle was wrong, but not both. All men are mortal. Therefore Aristotle was wrong.   (MM, AW)

Note that A_3 and A_6 have been omitted from the list in Group A of the preceding set of exercises. Before we prove the validity of A_3 and A_6, we shall establish a convention for the construction of truth tables involving more than two statement variables. A_3, for instance, uses three statement variables ($P, Q,$ and R); and A_6 uses four ($P, Q, R,$ and S).

In our previous truth tables, which involved only two statement variables (P and Q), the column for the second statement variable (Q) alternated as follows: TFTF; and the column for the first statement variable (P) alternated in pairs of T's and F's. Let us continue this type of serialization; and establish the convention that the column for the third from the last statement variable will alternate in quadruples of T's and F's; the column for the fourth from the last statement variable will alternate in octuples of T's and F's; etc. Thus, for three statement variables, the first three columns of a truth table will be as follows:

P	Q	R	
T	T	T	
T	T	F	
T	F	T	
T	F	F	
F	T	T	
F	T	F	
F	F	T	
F	F	F	

And, for four statement variables, the truth table will begin in this manner:

P	Q	R	S	
T	T	T	T	
T	T	T	F	
T	T	F	T	
T	T	F	F	
T	F	T	T	
T	F	T	F	
T	F	F	T	
T	F	F	F	
F	T	T	T	
F	T	T	F	
F	T	F	T	
F	T	F	F	
F	F	T	T	
F	F	T	F	
F	F	F	T	
F	F	F	F	

The number of (horizontal) rows in a truth table will always be 2^n, where n represents the number of variables involved.

EXERCISES

GROUP E

318. How many (horizontal) rows will there be in a truth table for a statement having n variables?
319. Prove, by the use of an abbreviated truth table, that A_3 is a valid argument form.
320. Prove, by the use of an abbreviated truth table, that A_6 is a valid argument form.

GROUP F

Prove the validity of each of the following arguments in two ways: (1) by the use of A_1 through A_{12}, and definitions; (2) by abbreviated truth tables. Use the suggested notation.

321. The Jones' are coming to dinner. If the Jones' are coming to dinner, I'm leaving. Therefore the Jones' are coming to dinner and I'm leaving. (J, L)
322. It is conceivable that the Jones' are coming to dinner and/or I'm not leaving; but if the Jones' actually *are* coming to dinner, I definitely *am* leaving! Hence the Jones' are coming to dinner or I'm not leaving (but not both). (J, L)
323. If ideas do not originate in sensation, then they originate in reflection. Hence ideas originate in sensation and/or they originate in reflection. (S, R)
324. Newton was right or his ethereal hypothesis is not correct, but not both. Hence, if Newton was right, then his ethereal hypothesis is correct. (N, H)
325. Snow is white and grass is green. Therefore grass is green and snow is white. (S, G)
326. If Arthur is going to marry Grace, Jane will be jealous. Arthur is going to marry Grace, and Grace will be happy. Therefore Jane will be jealous and Grace will be happy. (MG, JJ, GH)
327. If John marries Jane, Myra will be broken-hearted. Myra will not be broken-hearted. If John doesn't marry Jane, he will marry Myra. Therefore John will marry Myra. (MJ, MB, MM)
328. If Jane is cordial to Bruce, he will ask her to accompany him to the dance. If he will ask her to accompany him to the dance, Jane will not feel badly. Jane is cordial to Bruce. Hence Bruce will ask Jane to accompany him to the dance, and she will not feel badly. (JC, AD, FB)

329. Aristotle's ethical system has merit if, and only if, there are final ends. Dewey's ethical system has merit if, and only if, there is a continuum of means and ends. Aristotle's ethical system has merit and/or Dewey's ethical system has merit. Therefore there are final ends and/or there is a continuum of means and ends.   (A, FE, D, C)

330. If Bruce is insistent, Jane will give up smoking. If Bruce is foolish, he will let Jane have her own way. Either Bruce is insistent, or he will let Jane have her own way, but not both. Bruce will not let Jane have her own way. Hence Bruce is not foolish, and Jane will give up smoking.   (BI, GU, BF, OW)

§25.   The *Reductio ad Absurdum* Method of Proving Validity and Invalidity

In the preceding section, we ascertained that a deductive argument is valid if, and only if, its corresponding hypothetical conditional statement is always true; and that a deductive argument is invalid if, and only if, there is at least one F in the final column for the truth table of its corresponding hypothetical conditional statement.

The truth table method is easy to use when we are testing the validity or invalidity of an argument involving only a few atomic statements. But, the more atomic statements involved in an argument, the longer will be the truth table for its corresponding hypothetical conditional statement. It is cumbersome, and hence impractical, to construct truth tables for hypothetical conditional statements corresponding to arguments which involve several atomic statements; and hence a shorter method of proving validity and invalidity is desirable.

Let us see what is required by the truth table method of proving validity and invalidity, by examining a truth table which we previously constructed for the hypothetical conditional statement form corresponding to an argument form involving two statement variables, namely, the fallacy of affirming the consequent. If we can, by examination of this simple argument form, determine the characteristics of *any invalid argument form,* we can perhaps isolate these characteristics and find a shorter method of finding them in a longer argument. The abbreviated truth table for the hypothetical condi-

tional statement form corresponding to the fallacy of affirming the
consequent is the following:

$$[(P \supset Q) \cdot Q] \supset P$$

T T T T	T T
T F F F	T T
F T T T	F F	←——————
F T F F	T F

The arrow indicates the one case by virtue of which we can determine that the argument form is invalid. This is the case of a *true*
premise set being followed by a *false* conclusion. Remember that
the argument form has been tested for validity or invalidity by constructing a hypothetical conditional statement form with the operator
$\supset$ between the premise set and the conclusion of the original argument form. We know that a statement of the form $\cdots \supset$ — is false if,
and only if, the antecedent is true and the consequent is false. If the
consequent is true, the statement as a whole will be true no matter
what the truth value of the antecedent. The only case we must look
for, then, when we are testing for validity and invalidity, is that in
which the hypothetical conditional statement corresponding to the
argument has a false consequent and a true antecedent. A false consequent preceded by a *false* antecedent, on the other hand, is permissible. Let us, then, construct merely a *partial* truth table for the hypothetical conditional statement corresponding to an argument, ignor-
ing the cases in which the consequent is true (for in these cases the
statement as a whole will be true, no matter what the truth value
of the antecedent), and concern ourselves solely with those cases in
which the consequent is false. This method of testing for validity
and invalidity, which we shall explain, is known as "the *reductio ad
absurdum* method".

Using again as our example the fallacy of affirming the consequent, we shall indicate the truth value F under the horseshoe which
joins the premise set and the conclusion, in the hypothetical conditional statement form corresponding to the original argument
form:

$$[(P \supset Q) \cdot Q] \supset P$$

F

This indicates the case in which the hypothetical conditional statement form is false, and by virtue of which the corresponding argument form is invalid. Yet this case occurs if, and only if, the consequent of the corresponding hypothetical conditional statement form is false and its antecedent true. Let us accordingly put an F under the consequent, and try to ascertain if there is a case in which the antecedent is true.

$$[(P \supset Q) \cdot Q] \supset P$$
$$\overline{\ \text{F F}}$$

In order for the truth values thus far indicated to obtain, the conjunction of the premises of the original argument must be true. Let us therefore indicate a T in the appropriate place:

$$[(P \supset Q) \cdot Q] \supset P$$
$$\overline{\ \text{T} \quad \text{F F}}$$

We know further that this conjunction will be true if, and only if, each of its conjuncts is true. Let us accordingly indicate this:

$$[(P \supset Q) \cdot Q] \supset P$$
$$\overline{\ \text{T} \quad \text{TT} \ \ \text{F F}}$$

Let us now see what would be necessary for each conjunct to be true. Since the second conjunct is represented by a single variable Q, there is no problem. Q can be true or false, and in this case it must be true for the resulting conjunction to be true. As for the first conjunct, $P \supset Q$, however, this will be true in the following cases: (1) that in which P is true and Q is true, (2) that in which P is false and Q is true, and (3) that in which P is false and Q is false. Case (1) is excluded, because it requires that P be true, and we have already assigned to P the value *false* in the last column representing the conclusion of the argument. Case (3) is also excluded, because it requires that Q be false, and we have already assigned the value *true* to Q in the second member of the conjunction which represents the premise set of the original argument form. Case (2) is the only one which is permissible, because the truth values required of P and

Q do not conflict with truth values previously assigned to them. Let us therefore indicate case (2) in our truth table, as follows:

$$[(P \supset Q) \cdot Q] \supset P$$

$$\text{F T T T T F F}$$

We have thus shown that there is a possible case in which the hypothetical conditional statement form corresponding to the fallacy of affirming the consequent has the value *false*. This is the case represented by the one-row truth table above. Since this case is possible, the corresponding argument form is *invalid*.

If we should find it impossible to locate one case in which the hypothetical conditional statement corresponding to an argument were *false*, then we should conclude that the argument were *valid*. This is how this method of testing for validity and invalidity derives its name, *"reductio ad absurdum";* for it reduces to an absurdity the possibility of a false instance in the hypothetical conditional statement corresponding to a valid deductive argument. Such, for example would be the case with the argument form A_1. Let us construct a partial truth table, consisting of one row, for the hypothetical conditional statement form corresponding to this argument form, just as we did for the hypothetical conditional statement form corresponding to the fallacy of affirming the consequent, to test the validity of A_1. The hypothetical conditional statement form corresponding to A_1, we recall, is as follows:

$$[(P \supset Q) \cdot P] \supset Q$$

Let us look for a case in which this hypothetical conditional statement form would be false:

$$[(P \supset Q) \cdot P] \supset Q$$

$$\text{F}$$

If there is such a case, it will be that in which the consequent is false and the antecedent true. Let us indicate this in our truth table:

$$[(P \supset Q) \cdot P] \supset Q$$

$$\text{T   F F}$$

In order for the antecedent to be true, both conjuncts must be true. Let us also indicate this:

$$[(P \supset Q) \cdot P] \supset Q$$

$$\overline{}$$

T　　TT F F

Next we must decide in which cases the first conjunct, $P \supset Q$, can be true. The possible cases are those in which (1) P is true and Q is true, (2) P is false and Q is true, and (3) P is false and Q is false. Case (1) is excluded because it requires a truth value of Q which contradicts the truth value previously assigned to it. Case (2) is excluded because it requires truth values of P and Q which contradict the truth values previously assigned to them. And case (3) is also excluded because it requires a truth value of P which contradicts the truth value previously assigned to it.

Thus the row of the truth table which we are constructing for the corresponding hypothetical conditional statement form of A_1 cannot be meaningfully completed, inasmuch as it represents a contradictory case. We have reduced to an absurdity the possibility of there being a case in which the corresponding hypothetical conditional statement form of A_1 would have the value *false*. Hence A_1 is *valid*, and not *invalid*.

Since it is impossible to find a case, for the corresponding hypothetical conditional statement form of A_1, in which $P \supset Q$ could be true when the values for P and Q were such as would have to be assigned to make the argument form invalid, we indicate this in our truth table by drawing a line through the T under the $P \supset Q$, thus:

$$[(P \supset Q) \cdot P] \supset Q$$

$$\overline{}$$

$\cancel{T}$　　TT F F

This indicates that our row of the truth table, with the values required of P and Q for the argument form to be invalid, cannot meaningfully be completed; and that therefore the argument form is *valid*, inasmuch as its corresponding hypothetical conditional statement form is never false, i.e., is a tautology.

Thus far, the *reductio ad absurdum* method of proving validity and invalidity has been seen to be an easy one to use. A word of caution must, however, be voiced about its use; namely, there are arguments whose validity or invalidity cannot be ascertained by the assignment of merely *one* set of truth values to their corresponding hypothetical conditional statements. In these cases, we may have to perform the *reductio ad absurdum* test on two, or even more, possible assignments of truth values. Let us illustrate this in terms of an example. Consider the following:

$$(P \supset R) \supset (P \textcircled{v} R)$$

This hypothetical conditional statement form corresponding to an argument form must be assigned the value *false*, in order to test for validity by the *reductio ad absurdum* method:

$$(P \supset R) \supset (P \textcircled{v} R)$$

$$\overline{\phantom{(P \supset R) \supset (P \text{v} R)}}$$

F

This necessitates the assignment of the truth value, *true*, to the antecedent, and *false* to the consequent:

$$(P \supset R) \supset (P \textcircled{v} R)$$

$$\overline{\phantom{(P \supset R) \supset (P \text{v} R)}}$$

T   F   F

The three truth values which we have assigned are the only ones which we could possibly have assigned so far if we are to follow consistently the requirements of the *reductio ad absurdum* test for validity and invalidity. These truth values, we shall say, are *uniquely determined* by the requirements of the *reductio ad absurdum* test. The values for *P* and *R*, which we have not yet assigned, are *not* uniquely determined; rather there are various possible truth values for *P* and *R* which might be assigned to them without conflicting with the values already assigned. If we ignore this, we might mistakenly think we have completed our *reductio ad absurdum* test, and declare the argument form *valid*, by assigning F to *P*, and T to *R:*

$$(P \supset R) \supset (P \textcircled{v} R)$$

$$\overline{\phantom{(P \supset R) \supset (P \text{v} R)}}$$

F T T   F   F ⊬ T

In this case, the truth values cannot consistently be assigned, and we might be misled into thinking that the argument form is valid.

However, there are other possible truth values for P and R which can be consistently assigned, and which thus render the argument form invalid. Thus, for $P \circledV R$ to be false, there are two possible assignments of truth values to P and R. Let us indicate both of them in the following manner:

$$(P \supset R) \supset (P \circledV R)$$

$$\overline{}$$

$$\text{T} \qquad \text{F} \quad \begin{matrix}\text{T}\\\text{F}\end{matrix} \ \text{F} \ \begin{matrix}\text{T}\\\text{F}\end{matrix}$$

Finishing our assignment of truth values, we see that there are two cases which render the assignment of F to the hypothetical conditional statement form corresponding to our argument form possible, and which therefore reveal that the argument form is invalid, rather than valid, as we might previously have thought:

$$(P \supset R) \supset (P \circledV R)$$

$$\overline{}$$

$$\begin{matrix}\text{T}\\\text{F}\end{matrix} \ \text{T} \begin{matrix}\text{T}\\\text{F}\end{matrix} \ \text{F} \ \begin{matrix}\text{T}\\\text{F}\end{matrix} \ \text{F} \ \begin{matrix}\text{T}\\\text{F}\end{matrix}$$

The conclusion to be drawn from this discussion is that we must always be careful that we have examined all the relevant cases of possible assignment of truth values when using the *reductio ad absurdum* method of testing for validity and invalidity. Even if we have to test a few cases, this will nevertheless prove to be considerably quicker in most cases than constructing a complete truth table.

EXERCISES

Ascertain, by means of the *reductio ad absurdum* method, which of the following arguments are valid and which are invalid. For those arguments which are valid, construct proofs of validity using A_1 through A_{12}, as well as definitions if needed. Use the suggested notation.

331. The action of the B-complex vitamins is synergistic, or else it is not (but not both). Hence it is not the case that the action of the B-complex vitamins both is and is not synergistic.   (S)

332. If Jane does not study her logic, she will not pass the final examination. Hence, although Jane does not study her logic, she will pass the final examination.   (SL, PE)

333. Jones will not suffer from atherosclerosis if, and only if, he does not have an excess of cholesterol. Hence Jones has an excess of cholesterol and/or he will not suffer from atherosclerosis.   (A, C)

334. It is not the case that if oil is abundantly present in the stomach, then vitamin C can be adequately absorbed. Hence oil is abundantly present in the stomach only if vitamin C can be adequately absorbed.   (O, C)

335. If this animal is a dog, then it has fur; and if it is a cat, then it has fur. Therefore, if this animal has fur, then it is either a cat or a dog, but not both.   (D, F, C)

336. This patient's system can absorb an adequate amount of calcium if, and only if, his system contains enough vitamin D and enough vitamin F. His system does not contain enough vitamin D, and it does not contain enough vitamin F. Therefore this patient's system can absorb an adequate amount of calcium and/or his system contains enough vitamin D and enough vitamin F.   (C, D, F)

337. If the legislature will approve the new housing bill, then our war veterans will have adequate housing; and our war veterans will have adequate housing if the lobbyists exert pressure upon the legislature. Therefore, if the lobbyists exert pressure upon the legislature, then the legislature will approve the new housing bill.   (AB, AH, EP)

338. If one has a sufficient intake of lecithin, one will not have an excess of cholesterol. If one does not have an excess of cholesterol, then one need not fear senility. Hence, if one has a sufficient intake of lecithin, one need not fear senility.   (SI, EC, FS)

339. If the legislature will approve the new housing bill, then our war veterans will have adequate housing; and the legislature will approve the bill if the lobbyists exert pressure on the legislature. Hence our war veterans will have adequate housing only if the lobbyists exert pressure on the legislature.   (AB, AH, EP)

340. If the body lacks an adequate supply of vitamin D, then vitamin C cannot be adequately absorbed. If vitamin C is not adequately absorbed, one's resistance to the common cold is lowered. Hence, if one's resistance to the common cold is lowered, this means that the body lacks an adequate supply of vitamin D.   (LD, C, RL)

§26.   Proving Consistency and Inconsistency

Thus far we have learned how to distinguish valid from invalid argument forms. Suppose, however, we encounter an argument like the following:

EXAMPLE 76

> It is raining and it is not raining. If it is raining, Jane will go shopping.
> If it is not raining, Jane will not go shopping. Therefore Jane will go
> shopping and Jane will not go shopping.   (R, S)

We can easily prove that this is a valid argument, as follows:

EXAMPLE 77

$$\angle \therefore S \cdot \sim S$$

1. $R \cdot \sim R$	Pr.	
2. $R \supset S$	Pr.	
3. $\sim R \supset \sim S$	Pr.	
4. R	$1, A_7$	
5. S	$2, 4, A_1$	
6. $\sim R$	$1, A_8; A_7$	
7. $\sim S$	$3, 6, A_1$	
8. $\therefore S \cdot \sim S$	$5, 7, A_9$	

And again, by the use of the abbreviated truth table method, we
can prove that this argument is valid, thus:

EXAMPLE 78

$$\{[(R \cdot \sim R) \cdot (R \supset S)] \cdot (\sim R \supset \sim S)\} \supset (S \cdot \sim S)$$

T F F	F	T T F		T F	T	F
T F F	F	F F F		T T	T	F
F F T	F	T T F		F F	T	F
F F T	F	T F F		T T	T	F

Since the column indicated by the arrow contains all T's, the argument is valid.

But surely there is something wrong with this argument. We do
not ordinarily wish to be able to draw a self-contradictory conclusion, such as $S \cdot \sim S$, from a premise set. For that matter, we do not
wish our premise set to be self-contradictory, as ours is because it contains the self-contradictory premise, $R \cdot \sim R$. Yet there is no doubt
that the argument is valid, as we have proved. This will seem less

surprising if we recall a property of a valid deductive argument. If the premise or premise set of a valid deductive argument is true, then the conclusion is true. And indeed, if the premises of our argument, which include a self-contradictory statement, were true, then the conclusion, even though it may be self-contradictory, would also be true. The argument will never be *sound*, however, since there is no case in which all the premises and the conclusion can be true, as can be seen from an examination of the truth table for the hypothetical conditional statement corresponding to this argument.

What strikes us as odd about this argument, however, is this: it contains a self-contradictory premise, and a self-contradictory conclusion can be drawn from its premise set. An argument with a self-contradictory premise or premise set we shall call *"an inconsistent argument"*.

From an inconsistent premise or premise set (i.e., one involving a contradiction), *any* conclusion, including a self-contradictory one, can be drawn, by the use of A_{12} and A_4. Consider $P \cdot \sim P$ as representing a contradictory premise; then we may conclude *anything*, such as $Q \cdot \sim Q$, as follows:

$$/ \therefore Q \cdot \sim Q$$

1.	$P \cdot \sim P$	Pr.
2.	P	1, A_7
3.	$P \lor (Q \cdot \sim Q)$	2, A_{12}
4.	$\sim P$	1, A_8; A_7
5.	$\therefore Q \cdot \sim Q$	3, 4, A_4

Consistent arguments do not contain self-contradictory premises, nor can one draw a self-contradictory conclusion from the premises. All of our proofs of validity give us no assurance whatsoever that an argument is consistent. Yet consistency is obviously something which we should require of any argument. Accordingly, some test of consistency and inconsistency must be devised. Perhaps our knowledge of truth tables will assist us in the search for such a test.

Let us consider the corresponding hypothetical conditional statement form of an argument form which we have thus far assumed to be *consistent*, namely A_1. And let us compare its truth table with that of the corresponding hypothetical conditional of the inconsistent argument of Example 76.

EXAMPLE 79

Consistent Form

$$[(P \supset Q) \cdot P] \supset Q$$

T T T T	T	T
T F F F	T	F
F T T F	T	T
F T F F	T	F

       ↑   ↑ ↑

       1   2 3

EXAMPLE 80

Inconsistent Form

$$\{[(R \cdot \sim R) \cdot (R \supset S)] \cdot (\sim R \supset \sim S)\} \supset (S \cdot \sim S)$$

T F F F	T T F	T F	T	F
T F F F	F F F	T T	T	F
F F T F	T T F	F F	T	F
F F T F	T F F	T T	T	F

        ↑   ↑   ↑

        1   2   3

At first glance, there seems to be nothing crucially different between these two truth tables. They both reveal argument forms which are valid, as the arrows marked "2" show. Yet let us look at the truth tables for the premise sets of the two arguments, indicated by tne arrows marked "1". In the *consistent* form (Example 79), there is at least one case in which this column has the truth value T. In the *inconsistent* form (Example 80), however, all the cases in this column have the truth value F. And similarly for the conclusions of these two forms (indicated by the arrows marked "3"), the column for the conclusion of the *consistent* form (Example 79) contains at least one instance of the truth value T; whereas the column for the conclusion of the *inconsistent* form (Example 80) contains only instances of the truth value F. (Not all inconsistent arguments have contradictory conclusions, but a consistent argument will *never* have a contradictory conclusion.)

The column for the premise set of the *inconsistent* form (Example 80) never contains the truth value T, because an inconsistent premise set is always false. The simplest case of an inconsistent premise is one of the form $P \cdot \sim P$, which could in no instance be true.

A test for consistency and inconsistency suggests itself from these considerations. The conjunction which represents the premise set of an inconsistent argument is always false, inasmuch as the premise set is self-contradictory. Thus, for example, $P \cdot \sim P$ is always false, as we can show by the following truth table:

$$P \cdot \sim P$$

$$\begin{array}{ccc} T & F & F \\ F & F & T \end{array}$$

Accordingly, we may offer the following definition of "inconsistent deductive argument".

An inconsistent deductive argument is one whose corresponding hypothetical conditional statement has as its antecedent a contradictory statement.

Our discussion reveals, incidentally, that all inconsistent arguments must be valid; because their corresponding hypothetical conditional statements are tautologies, i.e., in their corresponding hypothetical conditional statements, false antecedents will always make the entire hypothetical conditional statement true.

All that we need do to see if an argument is consistent or inconsistent, is to test whether or not the antecedent of its corresponding hypothetical conditional statement is always false. If it is always *false,* the argument is *inconsistent.* If there is at least one case in which the antecedent of the hypothetical conditional statement is *true,* the corresponding argument is consistent.

The *reductio ad absurdum* method which we learned in the preceding section can be used to advantage in discovering whether or not an argument is consistent. Let us illustrate this with the inconsistent argument of Example 76. First, we write the conjunction which represents the premise set, thus:

$$[(R \cdot \sim R) \cdot (R \supset S)] \cdot (\sim R \supset \sim S)$$

Let us next try to find one case in which this conjunction can be true. (If we cannot, then the argument is inconsistent.) To indicate that we desire a true conjunction, let us place a T under the sign for the conjunction, thus:

$$\underline{[(R \cdot \sim R) \cdot (R \supset S)] \cdot (\sim R \supset \sim S)}$$
$$\text{T}$$

In order for this conjunction to be true, each of its conjuncts must be true. Let us also indicate this by adding the two T's which are marked with arrows below:

$$\overline{[(R \cdot \sim R) \cdot (R \supset S)] \cdot (\sim R \supset \sim S)}$$

$$\text{T} \qquad \text{T} \qquad \text{T}$$

Let us consider the first of these two conjuncts. In our example, this conjunct happens to be itself a conjunction. If it is to be true, each of *its* conjuncts must in turn be true. Accordingly, let us indicate this with two more T's, indicated by the numerals "1" and "2" below:

$$\overline{[(R \cdot \sim R) \cdot (R \supset S)] \cdot (\sim R \supset \sim S)}$$

$$\text{T} \qquad \text{T} \quad \text{T} \quad \text{T} \qquad \text{T}$$
$$(1) \qquad\qquad (2)$$

Again, the first of these conjuncts, marked by the numeral "1", is itself a conjunct. And again, it can be true if, and only if, each of *its* conjuncts is in turn true, as indicated by the addition of the two new T's labeled "a" and "b" below:

$$\overline{[(R \cdot \sim R) \cdot (R \supset S)] \cdot (\sim R \supset \sim S)}$$

$$\text{T T T T} \qquad \text{T} \qquad \text{T} \qquad \text{T}$$
$$\text{(a)} \quad \text{(b)}$$

At last we have discovered a contradiction in the premise set, for it is impossible for R (indicated by the "a") to be true at the same time that $\sim R$ (indicated by the "b") is true. Let us indicate that we have discovered the premise set of our argument to be self-contradictory by drawing a line through the T which represents the impossible case, thus:

$$[(R \cdot \sim R) \cdot (R \supset S)] \cdot (\sim R \supset \sim S)$$

TT T̸ T T T T

We have discovered, then, that the argument of Example 76 has a self-contradictory premise set, and may accordingly conclude that the argument is inconsistent.

A word of caution is here in order. Just because the truth table test (or the shorter, *reductio ad absurdum* test) reveals that an argument is *consistent*, we have no assurance that it is *valid*. For example, the argument "It is raining. Therefore Jane will go shopping." is consistent, because the premise is not self-contradictory; but it is not valid, as the following abbreviated truth table illustrates:

$$R \supset S$$

T T T
T F F
F T T
F T F

It need hardly be added that, as with the *reductio ad absurdum* test for validity, we shall again find cases in our tests for consistency in which we must test two or more possible assignments of truth values.

EXERCISES

GROUP A

341. Define "inconsistent deductive argument" in terms of "contradictory statement".
342. Why are not all consistent deductive arguments valid?
343. Why are all inconsistent deductive arguments valid?

GROUP B

For each of the following arguments, decide by the *reductio ad absurdum* method whether or not the argument is consistent. For those arguments which are *consistent*, ascertain further, by the *reductio ad absurdum* method, whether or not they are valid. Finally, for each argument that you have proved to be both consistent and valid by the *reductio ad absurdum* tests, construct a proof of its validity using A_1 through A_{12}, and definitions if needed. Use the suggested notation.

344. The action of the B-complex vitamins is synergistic. Therefore Jones should not take calcium. (AS, C)

345. The good is that toward which all things strive. Hence the good is that toward which all things strive if Aristotle's ethical theory is not wrong. (G, A)

346. Either Berkeley believed in the existence of objects or else he was an idealist, but not both. It is not true that if Berkeley believed in the existence of objects, then he was not an idealist. Hence, if Berkeley was an idealist, then he did not believe in the existence of objects. (EO, I)

347. If Jones likes brewer's yeast, then he can at present get an adequate supply of the B-complex vitamins. Jones likes brewer's yeast and/or he can at present get an adequate supply of the B-complex vitamins. Jones cannot at present get an adequate supply of the B-complex vitamins. Hence Jones does not like brewer's yeast. (LY, AS)

348. This object floats on water. Hence, if lead does not float on water, then this object floats on water if it is not lead. (OF, LF, OL)

349. If Copernicus was correct, then the universe is geocentric. If Kepler was correct, then the universe is geocentric. Hence Kepler was correct if Copernicus was correct. (CC, UG, KC)

350. If Jones takes enough brewer's yeast, then he gets an adequate supply of the B-complex vitamins. The following is not the case; namely, that if Jones does not have symptoms of a vitamin B deficiency, then he doesn't take enough brewer's yeast. Jones doesn't get an adequate supply of the B-complex vitamins. Hence Jones doesn't take enough brewer's yeast. (TE, AS, SD)

351. If the earth is the center of the universe, then Ptolemy was correct; whereas if the earth is not the center of the universe, then Copernicus was correct. The following is not the case; namely, that Copernicus was correct and/or Ptolemy was correct. Hence, if Ptolemy was not correct, then Copernicus was correct. (EC, PC, CC)

352. Plato was correct in his estimation of Socrates if, and only if, Socrates was a great philosopher. Aristotle was correct in his estimation of Plato if, and only if, Socrates was not a great philosopher. Either Aristotle was correct in his estimation of Plato, or else Plato was not correct in his estimation of Socrates, but not both. Therefore either Aristotle was correct in his estimation of Plato or else Socrates was not a great philosopher, but not both. (PC, SG, AC)

353. It is not true that this plant is an African violet and/or a rubber plant, and it is not a dahlia; only if the following is the case; namely, that it

is not a dahlia and that it isn't true that it isn't an African violet. It is not true that the following is not the case, namely, that this plant is a dahlia and/or not an African violet; moreover it isn't true that the following is not the case, namely, that this plant is both not a dahlia and not a rubber plant. Therefore this plant is an African violet.   (V, R, D)

354. The universe is geocentric if, and only if, it is not heliocentric. The universe is geocentric or else the Ptolemaic system is erroneous, but not both. The universe is heliocentric or else the Copernican system is erroneous, but not both. Hence, if it is not true that the Copernican system is not erroneous, then the Ptolemaic system is not erroneous.   (G, H, P, C)

355. If sufficient calcium cannot be utilized by the body if vitamin D is not present, then a lack of vitamin D can be a factor in causing arthritis. We should all get enough sunlight if sun contains vitamin D, only if a lack of vitamin D can be a factor in causing arthritis. Hence, if sufficient calcium cannot be utilized in the body if vitamin D is not present, then we should all get enough sunlight if sun contains vitamin D.   (CU, DP, FA, GS, SC)

§27.   Logical Equivalence

Compare the abbreviated truth tables for the following two statement forms:

$P \lor Q$	$\sim P \supset Q$
T T T	F T T T
T T F	F T T F
F T T	T F T T
F F F	T F F F

These two statement forms have the same final column in their truth tables, as indicated by the arrows above. This indicates that they are logically equivalent. We may, accordingly, establish a general principle that *two statements are logically equivalent if, and only if, they have the same final column in their truth tables.*

We may designate the logical equivalence of these two statement forms by placing a triple bar between them, thus:

$$(P \lor Q) \equiv (\sim P \supset Q)$$

The triple bar is used to indicate logical equivalence, for, as we recall, one way in which $P \equiv Q$ is read in English is "P is logically equivalent to Q."

When constructing truth tables to prove the logical equivalence of two statements, we must be careful that each atomic statement is consistently assigned the same truth values in each truth table. Thus, to prove the logical equivalence of $P \supset Q$ and $\sim Q \supset \sim P$, we would construct truth tables in the following manner. First, we will construct the truth table for $P \supset Q$:

$$P \supset Q$$

T	T	T
T	F	F
F	T	T
F	T	F

Now, in constructing the truth table for $\sim Q \supset \sim P$, if we are to make a comparison with the first truth table, we must use the same column for P that we used the first time, thus:

$$\sim Q \supset \sim P$$

T
T
F
F

This we must do, even though P here is the second, rather than the first, statement variable, if we are to compare the two molecular statement forms consistently with respect to the truth values of their atomic constituents.

Next, we shall have to use the same column for Q that we used in the truth table for $P \supset Q$, for the same reason:

$$\sim Q \supset \sim P$$

T	T
F	T
T	F
F	F

Now that we have the values for the atomic constituents of our second molecular statement form, we can complete its truth table as follows:

$$\sim Q \supset \sim P$$

F T T	F T
T F F	F T
F T T	T F
T F T	T F

The final column for this statement form, which is marked with an asterisk, is the same as the final column for $P \supset Q$. Hence the two molecular statement forms, $P \supset Q$ and $\sim Q \supset \sim P$, are logically equivalent. This we accordingly indicate in the following manner:

$$(P \supset Q) \equiv (\sim Q \supset \sim P)$$

Now let us see what would happen if, in constructing our truth tables for these two molecular statement forms, we were to have the *same* column for the first atomic member of each, and the *same* column for the second atomic member of each, with no regard for the fact that the first atomic member is different in each, and with no regard for the fact that the second atomic member is different in each:

$$P \supset Q \qquad\qquad \sim Q \supset \sim P$$

T T T	F T T F T
T F F	F T T T F
F T T	T F F F T
F T F	T F T T F

Now the final column for the first molecular statement form is different from the final column for the second molecular statement form. Because the truth tables are faultily constructed, with inconsistent assignments of truth values for the same atomic constituents, these truth tables would lead us to the incorrect conclusion that $P \supset Q$ and $\sim Q \supset \sim P$ are not logically equivalent.

The reason we must use the same column for identical atomic constituents when comparing the truth tables of two molecular statements to ascertain whether or not the molecular statements are logically equivalent is that, in effect, we are constructing a short-hand truth table for the statement constructed by inserting a triple bar between the two molecular statements in question, thus (where S_1 represents the first molecular statement, and S_2 represents the second):

$$S_1 \equiv S_2$$

We are merely omitting the final column under the $\equiv$, for, when S_1 and S_2 have the same final column in their truth tables, then the value under the $\equiv$ would always be T. However, if we bear in mind that we are really trying to ascertain whether or not $S_1 \equiv S_2$ is a tautology, then we will realize that, in this single biconditional statement form, every atomic constituent must always be assigned the same column of truth values wherever it occurs, whether in S_1 or in S_2.

If we are always careful to have exactly the same column for identical atomic statements when comparing truth tables of two molecular statements, we shall have no difficulty in deciding whether the molecular statements under consideration are or are not logically equivalent.

Note, incidentally, that all of the valid argument forms, A_1 through A_{12}, which involve only *two* variables, P and Q, are logically equivalent, since their corresponding hypothetical conditional statement forms all have the same final column in their truth tables, namely:

$$T$$
$$T$$
$$T$$
$$T$$

Thus, in more elaborate logical systems than the one we are presenting here, the equivalent forms can be derived from A_1, *modus ponens.*

Exercises

GROUP A

356. Explain how you would construct a *reductio ad absurdum* test for the logical equivalence of two statements.

357. Why are all of the valid argument forms, A_1 through A_{12}, which involve only two variables, logically equivalent?

GROUP B

Decide, by the use of abbreviated truth tables, which of the following pairs of statements are logically equivalent. Use the suggested notation.

358. (a) It is raining and/or the sun is shining.
     (b) The sun is shining and/or it is raining. (R, S)

359. (a) It is not the case both that Andrews is home and at work.
     (b) It is not the case both that Andrews is at work and at home. (H, W)

360. (a) The following is not the case; namely, that men are divine and/or gods are mortal.
     (b) Men are divine, although gods are not mortal. (M, G)

361. (a) It is not the case both that the soul is mortal and at the same time immortal.
     (b) The following is not the case; namely, both that the soul is immortal and that it is not the case that it is not mortal. (M, I)   .

362. (a) If that is a Buick, it is an automobile.
     (b) If that is not an automobile, then it is not a Buick. (B, A)

363. (a) It is not the case that we were served broccoli and/or cauliflower.
     (b) If we were served broccoli, then we were not served cauliflower. (B, C)

364. (a) It is not the case that we were served broccoli and/or cauliflower.
     (b) It is not the case that we were served cauliflower and/or broccoli. (B, C)

365. (a) The following is not the case; namely, that we were served cauliflower and not broccoli.
     (b) We were served cauliflower and/or broccoli. (C, B)

366. (a) If it's raining, I will wear a hat.
     (b) It is not raining and/or I will wear a hat. (R, H)

367. (a) If it's raining, I will wear a hat.
     (b) It's raining and/or I will wear a hat. (R, H)

368. (a) Jones is bald if, and only if, he lacks inositol.
     (b) It is not the case that Jones either is bald or lacks inositol (but not both). (JB, LI))

369. (a) Man is the measure of all things if, and only if, Protagoras was correct.
   (b) Man is not the measure of all things, or else Protagoras was correct, but not both.   (MM, PC)
370. (a) Arthur will help his father paint the house next summer if, and only if, he has free time.
   (b) Arthur will help his father paint the house next summer, or he won't have free time, but not both.   (HF, FT)
371. (a) John will marry Jane or he will marry Myra, but not both.
   (b) The following is not the case; namely, that John will marry Jane if, and only if, he marries Myra.   (MJ, MM)
372. (a) Grace's mother will grow to like Arthur or she will become indifferent, but not both.
   (b) Grace's mother will not grow to like Arthur if, and only if, she becomes indifferent.   (LA, BI)
373. (a) John will marry Myra or he will enter law school in the fall, but not both.
   (b) John will marry Myra if, and only if, he does not enter law school in the fall.   (MM, LS)
374. (a) It is not the case both that Arthur goes on the fishing trip with his father and does not say goodbye to Grace.
   (b) It is not the case both that Arthur says goodbye to Grace and does not go on the fishing trip with his father.   (FT, GG)
375. (a) John will not marry Jane and/or he will not marry Myra.
   (b) It is not the case both that John will marry Jane and that he will marry Myra.   (MJ, MM)
376. (a) John will not go to law school and Arthur will not join the Navy.
   (b) The following is not the case; namely, that John will go to law school and/or Arthur will join the Navy.   (LS, JN)
377. (a) It is raining and the sun is shining.
   (b) The sun is shining and it is raining.   (R, S)
378. (a) The following is not the case; namely, that lead is soft and/or it is heavy.
   (b) Lead is not soft, and/or it is not heavy.   (S, H)
379. (a) It is not the case both that lead is malleable and that it is brittle.
   (b) Lead is malleable and it is not brittle.   (M, B)
380. (a) If Myra doesn't go to the movies, she will miss a good show.
   (b) Myra will miss a good show and/or she will go to the movies.   (GM, MS)
381. (a) It is not the case both that lead is malleable and that it is brittle.
   (b) Lead is not malleable, but it is not brittle either.   (M, B)

382. (a) The following is not the case; namely, both that it is not raining and that the sun is not shining.
   (b) It is raining and the sun is shining.   (R, S)

383. (a) The following is not the case; namely, that this substance is not uranium and/or it is not radioactive.
   (b) This substance is uranium and/or it is radioactive.   (U, R)

384. (a) Either this capsule is a placebo or it contains morphine, but not both.
   (b) This capsule contains morphine, or it is a placebo, but not both. (P, M)

385. (a) This capsule is a placebo.
   (b) If this capsule is a placebo; then if it contains inert matter, then it is a placebo.   (P, IM)

386. (a) This capsule is a placebo.
   (b) If this capsule both is a placebo and contains inert matter, then it is a placebo.   (P, IM)

387. (a) The good is that at which all things aim if, and only if, Aristotle was right.
   (b) Aristotle was right if, and only if, the good is that at which all things aim.   (G, AR)

388. (a) If Aristotle was both wise and correct, then the good is that at which all things aim.
   (b) If Aristotle was wise, then if the good is not that at which all things aim, he was not correct.   (W, C, G)

389. (a) If Aristotle was both wise and correct, then the good is that at which all things aim.
   (b) If Aristotle was correct, then if the good is not that at which all things aim, Aristotle was not wise.   (W, C, G)

390. (a) If Aristotle was both wise and correct, then the good is that at which all things aim.
   (b) If Aristotle was wise, then if he was correct, the good is that at which all things aim.   (W, C, G)

391. (a) If Aristotle was wise, then if he was correct, the good is that at which all things aim.
   (b) If Aristotle was correct, then if he was wise, the good is that at which all things aim.   (W, C, G)

392. (a) The good is that at which all things aim; moreover Aristotle was wise and/or correct.
   (b) The good is that at which all things aim and Aristotle was wise; and/or: the good is that at which all things aim and Aristotle was correct.   (G, W, C)

393. (a) The good is that at which all things aim; moreover Aristotle was wise and/or correct.

   (b) The good is that at which all things aim and/or Aristotle was wise; moreover the good is that at which all things aim and/or Aristotle was correct.   (G, W, C)

394. (a) The good is that at which all things aim and/or Aristotle was both wise and correct.

   (b) The good is that at which all things aim and/or Aristotle was wise; moreover the good is that at which all things aim and/or Aristotle was correct.   (G, W, C)

395. (a) The good is that at which all things aim and/or Aristotle was both wise and correct.

   (b) The good is that at which all things aim and Aristotle was wise; and/or: the good is that at which all things aim and Aristotle was correct.   (G, W, C)

396. (a) The good is that at which all things aim and/or Aristotle was wise and/or correct.

   (b) The good is that at which all things aim and/or Aristotle was wise; and/or: the good is that at which all things aim and/or Aristotle was correct.   (G, W, C)

397. (a) The good is that at which all things aim, and Aristotle was both wise and correct.

   (b) The good is that at which all things aim and Aristotle was wise; moreover, he was correct.   (G, W, C)

398. (a) The good is that at which all things aim, and/or Aristotle was wise and/or correct.

   (b) The good is that at which all things aim and/or Aristotle was wise; and/or he was correct.   (G, W, C)

399. (a) Either Aristotle was wise or incorrect, but not both; or else the good is that at which all things aim, but not both.

   (b) Aristotle was wise, or else a necessary and sufficient condition for him being incorrect is that the good is not that at which all things aim, but not both.   (W, I, G)

GROUP C

400. Make a tabulation, in terms of P, Q, and R, of the logical equivalences which you establised in Group B. Indicate that two statement forms are logically equivalent by means of the triple bar. A sample follows:

$$(P \lor Q) \equiv (\sim P \supset Q)$$

When you have completed your tabulation, study the logical equivalences you have established until you are thoroughly familiar with them. A knowledge of them will facilitate the construction of proofs for the validity of the arguments which you will encounter in the next few sections.

§28. Using Logical Equivalences in Proofs of Validity

A great many arguments which are valid cannot be proved to be so just by the use of A_1 through A_{12} and the definitions. Yet they may be valid since some of the statements in their proofs of validity, though useless as they stand, may be logically equivalent to others which would make the completion of the proofs possible. Consider the following argument:

EXAMPLE   81

> If Jones doesn't buy a large quantity of this item, then he doesn't think it is properly priced. If he buys a large quantity, then he considers his dealer reliable. Therefore, if Jones thinks this item is properly priced, then he thinks his dealer is reliable.   (Q, P, R)

Symbolically, this would be translated as follows:

$$\sim Q \supset \sim P$$
$$Q \supset R$$
$$\therefore P \supset R$$

This argument is valid, because the first premise is logically equivalent to $P \supset Q$, as truth tables reveal. The conclusion would then follow by A_3. We can construct a formal proof of validity for this argument by noting what logical equivalence is utilized. The particular equivalence here involved is $(P \supset Q) \equiv (\sim Q \supset \sim P)$, which is known as "the *Principle of Transposition*". We can explain the Principle of Transposition thus: Two hypothetical conditional statements are equivalent when one of them asserts that the negation of the necessary condition of the other implies the negation of the sufficient condition of the other. In other words, the necessary condition of a hypothetical conditional statement does not obtain if, and only if, that for which it is necessary does not obtain.

In a proof, we may refer to the Principle of Transposition by the abbreviation "Trans". Thus, our proof for the validity of the argument of Example 79 would be constructed as follows:

$$/ \therefore P \supset R$$

1. $\sim Q \supset \sim P$ Pr.
2. $Q \supset R$ Pr.
3. $P \supset Q$ 1, Trans.
4. $\therefore P \supset R$ 3, 2, A_3

Note that, just as with the definitional equivalences, such as $P \vee Q =_{df} \sim(\sim P \cdot \sim Q)$, either member of *any* logical equivalence may be replaced by the other member, in a proof of validity. For example, if we are given $P \vee Q$, we can conclude $\sim(\sim P \cdot \sim Q)$, and give as our reason "D_I". Or, if we are given the second member of the definitional equivalence, $\sim(\sim P \cdot \sim Q)$, we can conclude the first member, $P \vee Q$, giving again as our reason "D_I". So, with the logical equivalences we now encounter, either member may be derived from the other. Thus, the argument of Example 81 required the derivation of the first member of the equivalence known as "the Principle of Transposition". One can as easily derive the second member of this equivalence from the first member, giving as the reason, "Trans".

Let us consider now another argument whose proof of validity will require that a statement in the proof by replaced by another statement which is logically equivalent to it:

EXAMPLE 82

If Jones thinks this item is properly priced and buys a large quantity of it, then he considers his dealer reliable. Therefore, if Jones thinks this item is properly priced, then he thinks his dealer reliable if he buys a large quantity.   (P, Q, R)

This would be translated symbolically as follows:

$$(P \cdot Q) \supset R$$
$$\therefore P \supset (Q \supset R)$$

As truth tables will reveal, these two statements are logically equivalent. The logical equivalence here involved, $[(P \cdot Q) \supset R] \equiv [P \supset (Q \supset R)]$, is called "the *Principle of Exportation*". We may explain this principle thus: In a hypothetical conditional statement containing three variables, if the necessary condition is itself a hypothetical conditional statement, then the conjunction of both statements of sufficient condition is the sufficient condition for the remaining variable. In other words, R is a necessary condition for the conjunction of P and Q if, and only if, R is a necessary condition for Q, and $Q \supset R$ is a necessary condition for P.

The Principle of Exportation shall be designated by the abbreviation "Exp" in our proofs of validity. Using this principle, we can easily construct a proof of validity for the argument of Example 82, as follows:

$$\diagup \therefore P \supset (Q \supset R)$$

1. $(P \cdot Q) \supset R$ Pr.
2. $\therefore P \supset (Q \supset R)$ 1, Exp

Next we wish to introduce two equivalences of commutativity, namely these:

1. $(P \circledV Q) \equiv (Q \circledV P)$
2. $(P \equiv Q) \equiv (Q \equiv P)$

Truth tables again will prove that these two statement forms do in fact represent logical equivalences. A_5 and A_8 already permit us to utilize two cases of commutativity, and we shall continue to refer to the commutativity of inclusive disjunction and conjunction, in our proofs of validity, by "A_5" and "A_8", respectively. For the two new cases of commutativity, namely those of exclusive disjunction and logical equivalence, let us refer to them in our proofs of validity by the abbreviation "Com".

Another group of logical equivalences which we shall consider involves the transformation from exclusive disjunctions to biconditional statements, and vice versa. These are of two kinds, as the following rule of transformation explains:

Rule for transforming exclusive disjunctions to biconditionals, and vice versa:
   To transform an exclusive disjunction to a biconditional, or vice versa, either:
   Case α: Change the sign of the whole expression, or
   Case β: Change the sign of one member.

The following logical equivalences illustrate this rule:

Case α: 1. $(P \equiv Q) \equiv \sim(P \circledV Q)$
          2. $\sim(P \equiv Q) \equiv (P \circledV Q)$

Case β: 1. $(P \equiv Q) \equiv (\sim P \ⓋQ)$
 2. $(P \equiv Q) \equiv (P \Ⓥ\sim Q)$
 3. $(\sim P \equiv Q) \equiv (P \ⓋQ)$
 4. $(P \equiv \sim Q) \equiv (P \ⓋQ)$

Truth tables easily establish all of these equivalences. They may be explained in the following manner: A biconditional statement and an exclusive disjunctive statement having the same two variables are logically equivalent if, and only if, either molecular statement is the negation of the other, or a member which is negative in one is positive in the other; because the members of a biconditional statement must have the same truth value, whereas those of an exclusive disjunction must not.

When employing, in a proof of validity, any one of these equivalences which obtain between biconditional statements and exclusive disjunctions, let us use the abbreviation "B/D"; "B" for "biconditional", "D" for "exclusive disjunction", and the slash, "/", to indicate transformation.

The final kind of logical equivalence which we wish to discuss in this section is encompassed by what is known as "the *Principle of Distribution*". Two logical equivalences are here involved:

 1. $[P \cdot (Q \vee R)] \equiv [(P \cdot Q) \vee (P \cdot R)]$
 2. $[P \vee (Q \cdot R)] \equiv [(P \vee Q) \cdot (P \vee R)]$

Both of these equivalences may be established by truth tables. The first of them may be explained as follows: The conjunction of any statement S, with an inclusive disjunction, is logically equivalent to the inclusive disjunction of S and the first member of the first disjunction, and S and the second member of the first disjunction; because either one or both members of the first disjunction may be true. The second equivalence of distribution may be explained in this manner: The inclusive disjunction of any statement, S, and a conjunction, is logically equivalent to the inclusive disjunction of S and the first member of the first conjunction, and the inclusive disjunction of S and the second member of the first conjunction; since at least one member of the initial disjunction is true, and accordingly the inclusive disjunction of S and either member of the first conjunction will be true.

Both of these equivalences of distribution shall be designated by the abbreviation "Dist", in proofs of validity.

Let us summarize the equivalences we have discussed in this section, and note their designations:

Designation	Name	Symbolic Statement
Trans	Transposition	$(P \supset Q) \equiv (\sim Q \supset \sim P)$
Exp	Exportation	$[(P \cdot Q) \supset R] \equiv [P \supset (Q \supset R)]$
Com	Commutativity	1. $(P \textcircled{v} Q) \equiv (Q \textcircled{v} P)$
		2. $(P \equiv Q) \equiv (Q \equiv P)$
B/D	Transformation of	Case α: 1. $(P \equiv Q) \equiv \sim(P \textcircled{v} Q)$
	Biconditional and	2. $\sim(P \equiv Q) \equiv (P \textcircled{v} Q)$
	Exclusive Dis-	Case β: 1. $(P \equiv Q) \equiv (\sim P \textcircled{v} Q)$
	junction	2. $(P \equiv Q) \equiv (P \textcircled{v} \sim Q)$
		3. $(\sim P \equiv Q) \equiv (P \textcircled{v} Q)$
		4. $(P \equiv \sim Q) \equiv (P \textcircled{v} Q)$
Dist	Distribution	1. $[P \cdot (Q \lor R)] \equiv [(P \cdot Q) \lor (P \cdot R)]$
		2. $[P \lor (Q \cdot R)] \equiv [(P \lor Q) \cdot (P \lor R)]$

Whenever we encounter a type of logical equivalence other than those enumerated above, we may designate it in a proof of validity by the catch-all designation, "LE", standing for "logical equivalence", and after this designation insert, in square brackets (or braces, if needed), the logical equivalence used, in terms of $P, Q, \cdots$, thus:

$$/ \therefore P$$

1. $\sim P \supset P$ Pr.
2. $\therefore P$ 1, LE $[(\sim P \supset P) \equiv P]$

Thus far we have been replacing a *complete* (not a *partial*) statement by one which is logically equivalent to it. In the section which follows, we shall consider the substitution of logically equivalent statements within a larger context.

Exercises

group A

401. In terms of necessary and sufficient conditions, explain the Principle of Transposition.
402. In terms of necessary and sufficient conditions, explain the Principle of Exportation.
403. Explain why the equivalences indicated by "B/D" obtain.
404. Explain why the equivalences of *distribution* obtain.
405. List three equivalences which are not discussed in this section; and show,

by the abbreviated truth table method, that they are, in fact, logical equivalences.

GROUP B

Construct a proof of validity for each of the following arguments, using A_1 through A_{12}, definitions, and the logical equivalences established in this section. Use the suggested notation.

406. This object is red if, and only if, it is not some other color. Therefore it is not the case that this object is both red and some other color.   (OR, OC)

407. This object is red if, and only if, it is not some other color. Therefore this object is red or it is some other color, but not both.   (OR, OC)

408. The following is not the case; namely, that Protagoras was correct although man is not the measure of all things, and/or Protagoras was not correct even though man is the measure of all things. Therefore Protagoras was correct or man is not the measure of all things, but not both. (P, M)

409. Either the soul is immortal or the soul is mortal (but not both). The soul survives the death of the body if, and only if, the soul is not mortal. Therefore, if the soul is immortal, it survives the death of the body.   (SI, SM, SD)

410. That Locke's theory of ideas is not wrong is a necessary and sufficient condition for the fact that ideas are not innate; moreover the idea of God comes from experience if, and only if, ideas are not innate. Thus the idea of God comes from experience and/or Locke's theory of ideas is wrong.   (TW, II, GE)

411. It is not the case that either the good is that at which all things aim or Aristotle was not correct in this respect, but not both. It is not the case that either Aristotle was not correct in this respect or that his ethical system still has value today, but not both. Therefore either the good is not that at which all things aim or Aristotle's ethical system still has value today, but not both.   (G, AC, V)

412. Jones should be careful to obtain a sufficient intake of lecithin if, and only if, he will develop atherosclerosis if he is deficient in it. Jones will not develop atherosclerosis; although he should revise his eating habits if, and only if, he should be careful to obtain a sufficient intake of lecithin and is deficient in it. Hence Jones does not need to revise his eating habits. (SI, A, D, EH)

413. That the science of nutrition is absurd is a necessary condition for the following not being the case; namely, that calcium is essential in the

human body and/or both vitamin D and vitamin F are necessary for its proper assimilation. The science of nutrition is by no means absurd. Therefore calcium is essential in the human body and/or vitamin F is necessary for its proper assimilation.   (NA, C, D, F)

414. Either Shakespeare was not a literary fraud or someone else wrote the plays attributed to him (but not both). Either Shakespeare was a literary fraud or he was a literary genius (but not both). Either someone else did not write the plays attributed to Shakespeare or the reputation accorded him by tradition is unjustified (but not both). Hence it is not the case both that Shakespeare was not a literary genius and that the reputation accorded him by tradition is not unjustified.   (LF, SW, LG, RU)

415. Either Shakespeare was a literary fraud or he was a great literary genius (but not both); and either Shakespeare was not a literary fraud or someone else wrote the plays attributed to him (but not both). Shakespeare was a great literary genius if, and only if, the reputation accorded him by tradition is justified. Therefore the reputation accorded Shakespeare by tradition is *not* justified, only if someone else wrote the plays attributed to him.   (LF, GG, SE, RJ)

416. Either Plato was not naïve in his opinion of Socrates, or Socrates was not a worthy philosopher (but not both). Either Plato was not ignorant or Plato was not wise (but not both). Plato was not ignorant if, and only if, Socrates was a worthy philosopher. Hence Plato was not wise if he was naïve in his opinion of Socrates.   (PN, SW, PI, PW)

417. Absolutism is correct; however, that absolutism is not correct is a necessary condition for the following not being the case; namely, that if Plato was correct, then the Doctrine of Ideas is tenable. Ethical relativism is correct or Plato was correct, but not both. Therefore that the Doctrine of Ideas is tenable is a necessary condition for the following not to be the case; namely, both that absolutism is correct and that ethical relativism is correct.   (A, P, DI, ER)

418. Jones can cure his night blindness only if he increases his intake of vitamin A; however, if he is not deficient in vitamin A, then he should not increase his intake of it. If Jones knows much about nutrition, then he has correct eating habits. Jones is not deficient in vitamin A and/or he does not have correct eating habits. Accordingly he does not know much about nutrition and/or he can't cure his night blindness.   (NB, II, D, N, EH)

419. If Protagoras was correct, then if man is the measure of all things, value is relative. That value is relative only if it is not absolute is a necessary and sufficient condition for ethical disputes. There are ethical disputes; and the following is not the case; namely, that either there are ethical

disputes or value is absolute, but not both. Hence the following is not the case; namely, that Protagoras was correct and man is the measure of all things.   (PC, MM, VR, A, ED)

420. We can predict the future if causal inferences are justifiable; and we can posit that the sun will rise tomorrow if we can predict the future. If reason cannot validate causality; then if experience cannot validate causality, the future is uncertain. Reason cannot validate causality. It is not the case both that causal inferences are not justifiable and that experience can validate causality. Therefore it is not the case both that the sun will not rise tomorrow and that the future is not uncertain.   (PF, IJ, SR, RV, EV, FU)

§29. The Principle of Substitution

In the preceding section, we learned that a *complete* statement may be replaced by one which is logically equivalent to it. Now we wish to carry this a step further, and allow the substitution of logically equivalent statements within a larger context. Thus, while we could previously replace an expression such as $P \supset Q$ by $\sim Q \supset \sim P$, when the expression occurred alone; we did not make the replacement in a larger context. But, since $P \supset Q$ and $\sim Q \supset \sim P$ are logically equivalent, the substitution of the one for the other in a larger context should be possible. For example, $X \supset (P \supset Q)$ should be logically equivalent to $X \supset (\sim Q \supset \sim P)$ (as can be shown by truth tables); and, further, such substitution within a larger context should be permitted. Let us therefore introduce what we shall call "the *Principle of Substitution*", to wit, that statements which are logically equivalent may be substituted for one another in a larger molecular statement.

When using this Principle of Substitution as a reason for a statement in a proof of validity, let us designate it by "S" (standing for "Substitution"), and indicate in parentheses (or square brackets or braces, as required) after the "S", which logical equivalence is being substituted. The logical equivalences shall, as before, be indicated by their appropriate designations (such as "Trans", "Com", etc.); or, if a name for the equivalence is wanting, the equivalence shall be written symbolically in terms of $P, Q,$ etc., in brackets (or braces) after the "S". We shall find that some equivalences not previously needed will now be employed with the Principle of Substitution, and shall be given appropriate designations. Let us illustrate one of these in terms of an argument for which we shall construct a proof of validity:

EXAMPLE 83

It is not the case that an ethical act is both wrong and right. Hence, if an ethical act is wrong, it is not right. (AW, AR)

The premise of this argument is translated as follows:

1. $\sim$(AW $\cdot$ AR)   Pr.

From this we must conclude AW $\supset$ $\sim$AR, which will have to be got from our premise by means of Definition II. But, according to Definition II, AW $\supset$ $\sim$AR should, in its unabbreviated form, read $\sim$(AW $\cdot \sim$ $\sim$AR), which is a different statement than our premise. If we could just double negate the AR of the premise, we could prove the validity of this argument. Yet we cannot double negate AR by A_{10}, for A_{10}, like the rest of our valid argument forms, is operative only on *complete* statements, and not on *partial* statements. And, in the premise of our argument, AR is part of a larger molecular statement. An attempt at diagramming an application of A_{10} will reveal that the argument form cannot be applied within a larger context.

Yet, to be sure, AR and $\sim$ $\sim$AR are logically equivalent statements, as we can easily demonstrate by truth tables. Let us therefore use the Principle of Substitution, and indicate the addition or the removal of a double negation within a larger context by "DN". Our proof of validity for the argument of Example 83, then, begins as follows:

$$\diagup \therefore \text{AW} \supset \sim\text{AR}$$

1. $\sim$(AW $\cdot$ AR)   Pr.
2. $\sim$(AW $\cdot \sim$ $\sim$AR)   1, S(DN)

We did not write "A_{10}" in parentheses after "S", because "A_{10}" does not indicate the *logical equivalence* of AR and $\sim$ $\sim$AR. "A_{10}" merely indicates that AR *implies* $\sim$ $\sim$AR, just as "A_{11}" merely indicates that $\sim$ $\sim$AR *implies* AR. This is quite a different matter from indicating that AR is *logically equivalent* to $\sim$ $\sim$AR, since *implication* is quite different from *logical equivalence.* And since the Principle of Substitution requires the substitution of *logically equivalent* statements, we indicated "S(DN)", in order to make sure that we were indicating the substitution of *logically equivalent* statements in our proof of validity for the argument of Example 83. Where A_{10} and A_{11} can be used, we shall indicate them, and reserve "S(DN)" for the case of substitution in a larger context.

Returning to our proof of validity, the conclusion of our argument can now be drawn directly from statement 2, thus:

    3. ∴ AW ⊃ ~AR   2, D_{II}

Let us examine another argument whose proof of validity involves the Principle of Substitution:

EXAMPLE 84

> It isn't the case that both Jane and Myra went to the theater. Hence, if Myra went to the theater, Jane didn't.   (J, M)

The premise of this argument is translated as follows:

    1. ~(J · M)   Pr.

From this we must conclude M ⊃ ~J. Now, applying what we earlier called "the backward method of proving validity", we see that in order to get this conclusion we shall have to have its definitional equivalent, namely ~(M · ~ ~J). There is no problem about double negating the J of the premise. We have already seen how this is done by S(DN). Let us, accordingly, do this:

    2. ~(~ ~J · M)   1, S(DN)

But we need ~ ~J and M in the reverse order so that we can conclude M ⊃ ~J. In other words, we need ~(M · ~ ~J) rather than ~(~ ~J · M). Our knowledge of the principle of commutativity will help us out here.

We cannot give "2, S(A_8)" as our reason for deriving ~(M · ~ ~J) from ~(~ ~J · M), because the valid argument forms apply only to complete statements, and not to partial ones. Further, the valid argument forms all express *inferences* from premise or premise set to conclusion, and do not express *logical equivalence,* which is required when using the Principle of Substitution. Let us therefore designate *all* the equivalences of commutativity by "S(Com)" when used with the Principle of Substitution. We will now have four such equivalences:

1. $(P \cdot Q) \equiv (Q \cdot P)$
2. $(P \vee Q) \equiv (Q \vee P)$
3. $(P \circledV Q) \equiv (Q \circledV P)$
4. $(P \equiv Q) \equiv (Q \equiv P)$

The first two of these will be used *only* with the Principle of Substitution, since A_8 and A_5, respectively, suffice in their stead when the Principle of Substitution is not needed.

We can now continue our proof of the validity of the argument of Example 84:

3. $\sim(M \cdot \sim \sim J)$ 2, S(Com)

Now the desired conclusion readily follows:

4. $\therefore M \supset \sim J$ 3, D_{II}

Steps 2 and 3 of the proof of the validity of the argument of Example 84 could be condensed, by the abbreviated method of proof, into one step, giving as the reason "1, S(DN, Com)," as is shown in the following abbreviated proof:

$$/ \therefore M \supset \sim J$$

1. $\sim(J \cdot M)$ Pr.
2. $\sim(M \cdot \sim \sim J)$ 1, S(DN, Com)
3. $\therefore M \supset \sim J$ 2, D_{II}

We shall give another illustration of an argument whose proof of validity involves the substitution of the logical equivalences indicated by "DN" and "Com":

EXAMPLE 85

If an ethical act is right, it is not wrong; and if the intent of the act is unworthy, the act is contemnable. It is not the case both that an ethical act is not right and that the intent of the act is not unworthy. Hence, it is not true both that an ethical act is not contemnable and that it is wrong.   (R, W, U, C)

The proof of the validity of this argument follows:

EXAMPLE 86

$$/ \therefore \sim(\sim C \cdot W)$$

1. $(R \supset \sim W) \cdot (U \supset C)$	Pr.	
2. $\sim(\sim R \cdot \sim U)$	Pr.	
3. $R \supset \sim W$	1, A_7	
4. $U \supset C$	1, A_8; A_7	
5. $R \vee U$	2, D_I	
6. $\sim W \vee C$	3, 4, 5, A_6	
7. $\sim(\sim \sim W \cdot \sim C)$	6, D_I	
8. $\therefore \sim(\sim C \cdot W)$	7, S(DN, Com)	

The introduction of the Principle of Substitution allows us to shed some new light on the equivalences of commutativity. Consider for a moment the four logical equivalences involved:

1. $(P \cdot Q) \equiv (Q \cdot P)$
2. $(P \vee Q) \equiv (Q \vee P)$
3. $(P \circledv Q) \equiv (Q \circledv P)$
4. $(P \equiv Q) \equiv (Q \equiv P)$

It is interesting that, of these four equivalences of commutativity, only the first is really required in our logic, since the other three can be derived from it. Thus, to see how one would establish (2) by the aid of (1), let us consider that $P \vee Q$ is definitionally equivalent to $\sim(\sim P \cdot \sim Q)$. By S(Com), this becomes $\sim(\sim Q \cdot \sim P)$, which is definitionally equivalent to $Q \vee P$. Similarly, we can proceed in reverse from $Q \vee P$ to $P \vee Q$. Either way we proceed, when we change $\sim(\sim P \cdot \sim Q)$ to $\sim(\sim Q \cdot \sim P)$ (or vice versa), we are merely using the principle of the commutativity of conjunction, illustrated by (1) above.

Let us see how one would establish (3) by using the principle of commutativity of conjunction. We know that $P \circledv Q$ is definitionally equivalent to $\sim(\sim P \cdot \sim Q) \cdot \sim(P \cdot Q)$. Applying S(Com) to each half of this conjunction, we arrive at $\sim(\sim Q \cdot \sim P) \cdot \sim(Q \cdot P)$, which is definitionally equivalent to $Q \circledv P$. Or we could proceed in reverse from $Q \circledv P$ to $P \circledv Q$.

Likewise, the fourth of these equivalences of commutativity can be established simply by reference to the principle of the commutativity of conjunction. For, by definition, $P \equiv Q$ is equivalent to $\sim(P \cdot \sim Q)$ $\cdot \sim(Q \cdot \sim P)$, which, by A_8, implies $\sim(Q \cdot \sim P) \cdot \sim(P \cdot \sim Q)$. This, by definition, becomes $Q \equiv P$. Similarly, we could derive $P \equiv Q$ from $Q \equiv P$ with reference to just the principle of the commutativity of conjunction.

In a proof of validity, then, some cases of S(Com) could be further explicated in terms of the commutativity of conjunction. But since all that the Principle of Substitution requires is that logically equivalent statements be substituted for one another, let us, for the sake of simplicity, in our proofs of validity, use the simple indication S(Com), for all four of the logical equivalences which illustrate the principle of commutativity, when used as a basis for substitution. S(Com) shall, of course, not be used when A_5 or A_8 could be used, just as S(DN) shall not be used when A_{10} or A_{11} could be used.

In addition to DN and Com, some other logical equivalences which shall be substituted according to the Principle of Substitution are the definitional equivalences indicated by our various definitions. Thus, in a proof of validity, we might encounter as a reason for a statement, "$S(D_1)$", thus:

$$/ \therefore \sim(X \vee Y)$$

1. $\sim \sim(\sim X \cdot \sim Y)$ Pr.
2. $\therefore \sim(X \vee Y)$ 1, $S(D_I)$

Here, the logically equivalent expressions, $\sim(\sim X \cdot \sim Y)$ and $X \vee Y$, are substituted for one another within the larger context indicated by the first tilde of the premise in the proof of validity above.

Definitions, no more than our valid argument forms, are operative on partial statements. Hence, if a logical equivalence established by a definition is the subject of a substitution within a larger context, the reason given must be "S" plus the specific definition which applies, as for example, "$S(D_I)$". However, if the definitions can be used by themselves without invoking the Principle of Substitution, we shall, as before, merely indicate the appropriate definition in our proof, without adding the designation "S".

Other possible substitutions within larger contexts are those designated by "Trans", "Exp", "B/D", and "Dist". Let us note, in this connection, that the introduction of the Principle of Substitution allows us to construct proofs for some of these equivalences. For example, the Principle of Transposition itself can be proved as follows:

Case α: $P \supset Q$ implies $\sim Q \supset \sim P$

$$\diagup \therefore \sim Q \supset \sim P$$

1. $P \supset Q$ Pr.
2. $\sim(P \cdot \sim Q)$ 1, D_{II}
3. $\sim(\sim Q \cdot P)$ 2, S(Com)
4. $\sim(\sim Q \cdot \sim \sim P)$ 3, S(DN)
5. $\therefore \sim Q \supset \sim P$ 4, D_{II}

Case β: $\sim Q \supset \sim P$ implies $P \supset Q$

$$\diagup \therefore P \supset Q$$

1. $\sim Q \supset \sim P$ Pr.
2. $\sim(\sim Q \cdot \sim \sim P)$ 1, D_{II}
3. $\sim(\sim \sim P \cdot \sim Q)$ 2, S(Com)
4. $\sim(P \cdot \sim Q)$ 3, S(DN)
5. $\therefore P \supset Q$ 4, D_{II}

Likewise, the Principle of Exportation can be proved by using the Principle of Substitution, thus:

Case α: $(P \cdot Q) \supset R$ implies $P \supset (Q \supset R)$

$$\diagup \therefore (P \cdot Q) \supset R$$

1. $(P \cdot Q) \supset R$ Pr.
2. $\sim[(P \cdot Q) \cdot \sim R]$ 1, D_{II}
3. $\sim[P \cdot (Q \cdot \sim R)]$ 2, S$\{[(P \cdot Q) \cdot R] \equiv [P \cdot (Q \cdot R)]\}$
4. $\sim[P \cdot \sim \sim (Q \cdot \sim R)]$ 3, S(DN)
5. $\sim[P \cdot \sim (Q \supset R)]$ 4, S(D_{II})
6. $\therefore P \supset (Q \supset R)$ 5, D_{II}

Case β: $P \supset (Q \supset R)$ implies $(P \cdot Q) \supset R$

$$\diagup \therefore (P \cdot Q) \supset R$$

1. $P \supset (Q \supset R)$ Pr.
2. $\sim[P \cdot \sim (Q \supset R)]$ 1, D_{II}
3. $\sim[P \cdot \sim \sim (Q \cdot \sim R)]$ 2, S(D_{II})
4. $\sim[P \cdot (Q \cdot \sim R)]$ 3, S(DN)
5. $\sim[(P \cdot Q) \cdot \sim R]$ 4, S$\{[P \cdot (Q \cdot R)] \equiv [(P \cdot Q) \cdot R]\}$
6. $\therefore (P \cdot Q) \supset R$ 5, D_{II}

It should be noted, in the interests of formal rigor, that even though these two principles were proved after they had been introduced, we are not guilty of circular reasoning, since the principles were in no way used in their own proofs.

One final word is in order before we begin the exercises which utilize the Principle of Substitution: Let us always remember the logician's demand for elegance, and in our proofs of validity, never use more when less will serve. Never write out an equivalence, symbolically, in a reason, when it has a ready designation, such as "Com". And never designate a logical equivalence when one of our twelve valid argument forms will suffice.

EXERCISES

Using A_1 through A_{12}, definitions, logical equivalences, and the Principle of Substitution, construct a proof of validity for each of the following arguments. Use the suggested notation.

421. The following is not the case; namely, that Aristotle's ethics has some merit if the good life is not desirable, and that the good life is not desirable if Aristotle's ethics has some merit. Hence the good life is desirable if Aristotle's ethics has some merit.   (AE, GL)

422. The following is not the case; namely, that Aristotle's ethics has some merit and/or the good life is desirable, and that the good life is desirable only if Aristotle's ethics does not have some merit. Hence the good life is desirable if Aristotle's ethics has some merit.   (AE, GL)

423. The following is not the case; namely, both that Plato was wrong, and that Aristotle didn't disagree with him although Aristotle was his student. Hence, if Plato was wrong and Aristotle was his student, then Aristotle disagreed with Plato.   (PW, AD, S)

424. If Jane goes to the club meeting; then Myra will go if, and only if, Grace goes. Hence Jane won't go to the club meeting if it isn't true that either Myra will go or Grace will not go (but not both).   (J, M, G)

425. It is not the case that Jane's account not being right is a necessary condition for the fact that Grace will marry Arthur only if he proposes marriage. Hence it is not the case that Jane's account being right is a sufficient condition for it not being the case that Grace won't marry Arthur if he doesn't propose marriage.   (JR, GM, AP)

426. It is not the case that John's account being right is a necessary condition for the fact that Grace will marry Arthur if he proposes marriage; and it is not the case both that John's account is not right and that it isn't true that Grace won't marry Arthur if he doesn't propose marriage. Hence the following obviously is not the case; namely, that Grace will marry Arthur if and only if he doesn't propose marriage.   (JR, GM, AP)

427. It is not many months later; but Arthur has proposed to Grace and she has not refused to marry him. Hence the following is not the case; namely,

that it is many months later, and/or Arthur hasn't proposed to Grace if she has not refused to marry him.   (MM, AP, RM)

428. If Jones takes the bioflavonoids and/or rutin, and ascorbic acid and/or the bioflavonoids, then he will not need to fear the common cold. Hence Jones will not need to fear the common cold if he takes the bioflavonoids and/or rutin and ascorbic acid.   (B, R, A, C)

429. Jane will not go to the club meeting or Grace will go, but not both. It is not the case both that Grace will go and that she will meet Arthur; and if Jane doesn't go, Myra will attend. Grace will meet Arthur. Hence Myra will attend the club meeting.   (J, G, A, M)

430. Grace and Jane will both go to the club meeting only if it doesn't meet on a Saturday night. Grace will go to the club meeting; and if many people plan to attend, Jane will go. Hence not many people plan to attend if the club meets on a Saturday night.   (G, J, SN, PA)

431. If it is not the case that if John goes bowling, Jane will attend the club meeting; then either Myra will attend the club meeting or Grace will, but not both. Therefore, if John goes bowling; then if Jane won't attend the club meeting, then Grace will attend if and only if Myra won't attend.   (JB, JA, M, G)

432. If the earth is round, it is not flat; and if the sun is hot, it gives heat. It is not the case both that the earth is not round and that the sun is not hot. Hence it is not true both that the sun does not give heat and that the earth is flat.   (ER, EF, SH, GH)

433. Jane won't go to the club meeting if the following is not the case; namely, that Myra won't go if it isn't true that if Grace goes to the club meeting, Arthur will go bowling. Hence, if Jane goes to the club meeting, then if Myra and Grace go, Arthur will go bowling.   (J, M, G, A)

434. The science of nutrition is absurd only if, if people practice it, then if they are serious they are misguided. Hence, if it is not the case that if people practice nutrition and are serious, only if they are misguided, then the science of nutrition is not absurd.   (NA, PP, S, M)

435. The following is not the case; namely, that the external world exists if and only if Berkeley is right. Berkeley is right only if his doctrine that "to be is to be perceived" is correct. Everyone will agree with Berkeley if his doctrine that "to be is to be perceived" is correct; however, it is not the case that everyone will agree with Berkeley. Hence the external world exists. (EW, BR, DC, EA)

436. The following is not the case; namely, that protein is essential in the human diet or else brewer's yeast being a poor source of protein is a sufficient condition for the fact that if one is deficient in protein there is cause for alarm, but not both. Therefore that protein is essential in the human diet is a sufficient condition for the fact that there is no cause for alarm

only if it isn't true both that one is deficient in protein and brewer's yeast is a poor source.   (PE, BY, DP, CA)

437. The following is not the case; namely, that vitamin C is dangerous and/or rose hips and potatoes are both rich in this vitamin. Vitamin C is dangerous if the following is not the case; namely, both that rose hips are rich in it, and that citrus fruits and/or potatoes are rich in this vitamin. Hence the following is not the case; namely, that citrus fruits aren't rich in vitamin C if rose hips are rich in it.   (CD, RH, P, CF)

438. The good life is desirable if, and only if, Aristotle was not correct and/or Plato was correct. The following is not the case; namely, that Plato was correct and/or Socrates was correct. If the good life is desirable only if Aristotle was not correct, then Socrates was correct and/or there are divergent views on ethics. Hence there are divergent views on ethics.   (GL, A, P, S, DV)

439. The veracity of God implies the certainty of geometry. If God is deceitful, we cannot be sure of anything; and if philosophers are correct, then follows His veracity or His deceitfulness (but not both). Philosophers are correct if they think this is an important problem; and they think this is an important problem. Therefore it is not the case both that geometry is not certain and that we can be sure of anything.   (VG, CG, GD, SA, PC, IP)

440. The following is not the case; namely, both that ideas are innate and that it is not the case that if Locke is right the idea of God originates in experience. That ideas aren't innate is a sufficient condition for British empiricism having a reliable foundation. That Locke's *Essay concerning Human Understanding* is hopelessly inaccurate is a necessary condition for the fact that the following is not the case; namely, that Cartesian theory of knowledge is correct and/or British empiricism doesn't have a reliable foundation. It is not the case that Locke's not being right is a necessary condition for the following not being the case; namely, that Locke's *Essay* is hopelessly inaccurate and/or the Cartesian theory of knowledge is correct. Hence the idea of God originates in experience.   (II, LR, OE, RF, EI, CT)

§30.   The Conditional Method of Proving Validity

So far we have encountered basically two methods of proving validity. The first method is that in which we write down each statement deductively derived from the premises of an argument, or from the premises and other derived statements, or simply from other derived statements, until we arrive at the desired conclusion of the argument; and in which we utilize our various valid argument forms, the definitions, logical equivalences, and the Principle of Substitution; referring to these principles as justifying reasons for each statement involved in the proof. This step-by-step method of proving the validity of an argument we shall call "the construction of a *formal* proof", using the term "formal proof" to indicate the resulting proof of validity. The second method we studied is that which employs truth tables, and has been called "the truth table method". A variant of this method is that in which just a few truth values need be assigned, and which has been called the *"reductio ad absurdum* method".

Two more methods of proving validity, or rather one method and a variant, need yet to be discussed. The method we wish to consider in this section is called "the *conditional method* of proving validity" (the resulting proof being called, accordingly, "a conditional proof"); and its variant, which we shall discuss in the next section, is called "the *indirect method* of proving validity" (the resulting proof being called, accordingly, an "indirect proof").

Of these various methods of proving the validity of an argument, the truth table method and its variant, the *reductio ad absurdum* method, alone are useful in proving *invalidity*. If we cannot construct a *formal* proof of validity for an argument, this in no way assures us that the argument is invalid. It may simply be that we have not hit upon the right principle to invoke to prove its validity. The truth table method and its variant, however, can provide conclusive evidence that an argument is invalid, because they demonstrate the impossibility of the premise or premise set always implying the conclusion (i.e., they locate at least one F in the final column for the hypothetical conditional statement corresponding to the argument). The method of constructing a *formal* proof is nevertheless an invaluable tool, because, when an argument is valid, this method is frequently easier than is the truth table method or the *reductio ad absurdum* method, as should be evident to the reader by now.

The conditional method is quite similar to the method in which a formal proof is constructed, in that it also proceeds in step-by-step fashion; but it is even easier to use, in many cases, that is the method of constructing a formal proof. The conditional method may be used only for an argument whose conclusion is either a hypothetical conditional statement or equivalent to a hypothetical conditional statement, however. If we let the symbol P stand for "premise or premise set", and $X \supset Y$ stand for a hypothetical conditional statement which is the conclusion of an argument, then we may say that the conditional method may be used only for arguments of the following form:

$$P$$
$$\therefore X \supset Y$$

or for arguments whose conclusions are of a form equivalent to the form $X \supset Y$, such as $\sim X \vee Y$ or $\sim(X \cdot \sim Y)$.

For such an argument, we assume X, and then prove that Y follows from P and X. Let us use "I" and "II" to designate these two argument forms:

I	II
P	P
$\therefore X \supset Y$	X
	$\therefore Y$

Argument form I is that whose validity we wish to prove. We do this, according to the conditional method, by proving form II valid.

Let us see why this is justified. For every argument, there corresponds a hypothetical conditional statement, as we already know. Corresponding to form I would be the hypothetical conditional statement form $P \supset (X \supset Y)$, and corresponding to form II would be $(P \cdot X) \supset Y$. These two statement forms are logically equivalent, as truth tables reveal. The particular equivalence involved is, in fact, what we have called "the Principle of Exportation". Since these two statement forms are equivalent, their corresponding argument forms are equivalent. This, then, is the justification of the conditional method of proving validity.

Now that the conditional method has been explained and a justification has been given for it, we shall introduce certain notational conventions for the construction of conditional proofs of validity. Let us do this by considering two arguments of the English language, and see what is involved in constructing a conditional proof of the validity of each. The first argument follows:

EXAMPLE 87

Grace will meet Arthur for lunch downtown if she goes snopping, only
if it is a clear day. Hence, if it's not a clear day, then she won't meet
Arthur.   (M, S, C)

Symbolically, this argument is translated as follows:

$$(S \supset M) \supset C$$
$$\therefore \sim C \supset \sim M$$

Let us begin our conditional proof of the validity of this argument as we would a formal proof, namely by writing the premise
and the conclusion thus:

$$\underline{/ \therefore \sim C \supset \sim M}$$

1. $(S \supset M) \supset C$ Pr.

We shall next write as an assumption the antecedent, $\sim C$, of the
hypothetical conditional conclusion of the argument, and indicate
that we shall then prove that the consequent of the hypothetical
conditional conclusion, namely $\sim M$, follows. We shall indent the
line giving our assumption; and in the "reasons" column after it
write "Assump" (for "assumption"), and indicate that we shall now
derive $\sim M$, thus:

$$\underline{/ \therefore \sim C \supset \sim M}$$

1. $(S \supset M) \supset C$ Pr.
2. $\sim C$ Assump $\underline{/ \therefore \sim M}$

The line of every following statement derived from the original
premise and the assumption will also be indented, thus:

EXAMPLE 88

Conditional Proof of the Validity of the Argument of Example 85

$$\underline{/ \therefore \sim C \supset \sim M}$$

1. $(S \supset M) \supset C$ Pr.
2. $\sim C$ Assump $\underline{/ \therefore \sim M}$
3. $\sim(S \supset M)$ 1, 2, A_2
4. $\sim\sim(S \cdot \sim M)$ 3, $S(D_{II})$
5. $S \cdot \sim M$ 4, A_{11}
6. $\sim M \cdot S$ 5, A_8

7. ~M   6, A₇

8. ∴ ~C ⊃ ~M   2–7, CP

Statement 8 of the above proof has *not* been indented, because it states that from the assumption of statement 2 (plus the original premise), what was to be proved to follow (i.e., ~M) does in fact follow. The reason given for statement 8, namely "2–7, CP", is interpreted to mean "statements 2 through 7, in which the method of conditional proof is used, plus the original premise, justify statement 8." Statement 8 should not be indented since it is not within what shall be called "the scope of the assumption", i.e., it is not dependent on the assumption.

Statements 1 through 7 of this proof constitute the conditional proof of the validity of the original argument (i.e., they constitute a *formal* proof of the validity of an argument equivalent to the original one). Statement 8 merely recapitulates the conclusion of the original argument and informs us that, since statements 1 through 7 constitute a proof of the validity of an argument equivalent to the original one, the conclusion of the original argument accordingly follows from the premise of the original argument.

Suppose the conclusion of the original argument had been C V ~M instead of ~C ⊃ ~M. Then, the ∴ would have been omitted from statement 8, and the proof would proceed to C V ~M by means of Definitions II and I, in that order.

It will be interesting, before we examine our second English argument, to compare the length of the conditional proof of the validity of the first argument, as given in Example 88, with that of the standard *formal* proof of its validity. The abbreviated proof is not used, so that it is evident how many operations are involved:

EXAMPLE 89

Formal Proof of the Validity of the Argument of Example 85

$$/ \therefore \sim C \supset \sim M$$

1. (S ⊃ M) ⊃ C   Pr.
2. ~C ⊃ ~(S ⊃ M)   1, Trans
3. ~C ⊃ ~ ~(S · ~M)   2, S(D_{II})
4. ~C ⊃ (S · ~M)   3, S(DN)
5. ~[~C · ~(S · ~M)]   4, D_{II}
6. C V (S · ~M)   5, D_I

7. $(C \lor S) \cdot (C \lor \sim M)$	6, Dist
8. $(C \lor \sim M) \cdot (C \lor S)$	7, A_8
9. $C \lor \sim M$	8, A_7
10. $\sim(\sim C \cdot \sim \sim M)$	9, D_I
11. $\therefore \sim C \supset \sim M$	10, D_{II}

Not only is this formal proof longer than the conditional proof, it is also much more complicated and more difficult to construct.

The second English argument whose validity we wish to prove by the conditional method involves an assumption within the scope of another assumption. The second assumption and the statements within its scope will be indented further than the first indentation. The argument follows:

EXAMPLE 90

If Grace goes shopping downtown, then she will meet Arthur for lunch if it doesn't rain. If it doesn't rain, then she will have a good time if she meets Arthur. Hence, if Grace goes shopping, she will have a good time if it doesn't rain.   (S, M, R, T)

The conditional proof of the validity of this argument follows:

EXAMPLE 91

$$/ \therefore S \supset (\sim R \supset T)$$

1. $S \supset (\sim R \supset M)$	Pr.	
2. $\sim R \supset (M \supset T)$	Pr.	
3. S	Assump $/ \therefore \sim R \supset T$	
4. $\sim R$	Assump $/ \therefore T$	
5. $M \supset T$	2, 4, A_1	
6. $\sim R \supset M$	1, 3, A_1	
7. $\sim R \supset T$	6, 5, A_3	
8. T	7, 4, A_1	
9. $\sim R \supset T$	4–8, CP	
10. $\therefore S \supset (\sim R \supset T)$	3–9, CP	

Exercises

group A

441. What is meant by "formal proof"?

442. Explain why the method of conditional proof is justified.
443. By what method or methods may one prove invalidity? Why are other methods inadequate to prove invalidity?
444. Construct a formal proof of the validity of the argument of Example 88.
445. Following is a list of numbers of exercises from the preceding section. You have already constructed formal proofs for the validity of the arguments of these exercises. Now construct a conditional proof of the validity of each:

421	431
422	432
424	433
428	436
430	439

GROUP B

For each of the following arguments, construct both a formal and a conditional proof of validity, using the suggested notation:

446. If Arthur will like the dress if Grace buys it, then Grace will be pleased. Thus, Grace will not be pleased only if Arthur will not like the new dress. (AL, GB, GP)
447. If Grace goes shopping downtown, then if it doesn't rain she will meet Arthur for lunch. It is not true that Grace won't go shopping downtown and/or won't meet Arthur for lunch. Hence Grace will meet Arthur for lunch if it doesn't rain. (GS, R, MA)
448. If Grace is going to buy a dress like Jane's, then Jane will be furious only if Arthur likes Grace's new dress. If Jane will be furious, this means that Grace is going to buy a dress like Jane's. Hence, if Jane will be furious, this means that Arthur will like Grace's new dress. (BD, JF, AL)
449. If Grace goes shopping downtown, then if she sees a new dress she will buy it. If she sees a new dress, her mother will accuse her of being extravagant if she buys it. Therefore, if Grace goes shopping downtown, her mother will accuse her of being extravagant if she sees a new dress. (GS, SD, B, MA)
450. If Grace's mother is going to accuse Grace of being extravagant, then if Jane is furious as well, Arthur will be certain to tell Grace he likes her new dress. Grace's mother is going to accuse her of being extravagant and/or Grace will return the dress. Hence Grace will not return the dress even though Jane is furious, only if Arthur will be certain to tell Grace he likes her new dress. (MA, JF, AT, RD)

§31.   The Indirect Method of Proving Validity

The indirect method of proving validity is, as we mentioned in the preceding section, a species of the conditional method. Like the conditional method, it proceeds in step-by-step fashion from the premise or premise set of an argument, *plus an assumption,* to the conclusion. It is the nature of the assumption, however, which distinguishes this method from the conditional method which we described earlier. The assumption which one makes is the *negation* of the conclusion of the argument.

Let us use "I" to designate the form of any argument, where P designates its premise or premise set, and C its conclusion; and let us use "II" to designate the logically equivalent argument form whose validity will be proved by the indirect method. These two argument forms will then be as follows:

$$
\begin{array}{cc}
\underline{\quad I \quad} & \underline{\quad II \quad} \\
P & P \\
\therefore C & \sim C \\
& \therefore C
\end{array}
$$

From the conclusion of I, by the principle of addition (A_{12}), we can derive $C \lor C$, which is logically equivalent to C, as may be shown by truth tables. By Definitions I and II, in that order, we may transform $C \lor C$ to $\sim C \supset C$. Thus, since C and $\sim C \supset C$ can be derived from the same premise set, and since C and $\sim C \supset C$ are logically equivalent, the argument form with premise set P, from which the conclusion C is derived (form I), is logically equivalent to an argument form with the same premise set P from which the conclusion $\sim C \supset C$ is derived. This other argument form, which we shall designate "III", is:

$$
\begin{array}{c}
\underline{\quad III \quad} \\
P \\
\therefore \sim C \supset C
\end{array}
$$

So far, we have shown that I and III are logically equivalent argument forms, but have not said why II is logically equivalent to I. However, a formal proof of the validity of II is a conditional proof of the validity of III, whereby II is logically equivalent to III. And since I and III are also logically equivalent argument forms, it follows that I and II are logically equivalent argument forms. We shall say that a formal proof of the validity of II is an indirect proof of the validity of I.

Such, then, is the justification of the indirect method of proving validity. Exactly how we construct an indirect proof of validity is best ascertained by examining an indirect proof of the validity of an argument in the English language. The argument which we shall examine follows:

EXAMPLE 92

If Arthur lives on Quincy Street, then he will go downtown only if he gets a ride. If Arthur owns a tuxedo, then it is not true both that he will go downtown and gets a ride. Therefore the following is not the case; namely, that Arthur goes downtown, and both lives on Quincy Street and owns a tuxedo.   (Q, D, R, T)

We shall present the indirect proof of the validity of this argument, and then explain in detail what is involved in the construction of the proof. The proof follows:

EXAMPLE 93

$$/ \therefore \sim[D \cdot (Q \cdot T)]$$

1.	$Q \supset (D \supset R)$	Pr.
2.	$T \supset \sim(D \cdot R)$	Pr.
3.	$\sim \sim[D \cdot (Q \cdot T)]$	Assump (IP)
4.	$D \cdot (Q \cdot T)$	$3, A_{11}$
5.	$(Q \cdot T) \cdot D$	$4, A_8$
6.	$Q \cdot T$	$5, A_7$
7.	Q	$6, A_7$
8.	$D \supset R$	$1, 7, A_1$
9.	D	$4, A_7$
10.	R	$8, 9, A_1$
11.	$T \cdot Q$	$6, A_8$
12.	T	$11, A_7$
13.	$\sim(D \cdot R)$	$2, 12, A_1$
14.	$D \cdot R$	$9, 10, A_9$
15.	$(D \cdot R) \vee \sim[D \cdot (Q \cdot T)]$	$14, A_{12}$
16.	$\therefore \sim[D \cdot (Q \cdot T)]$	$15, 13, A_4$

Beginning with statement 3 of this proof, the statements which follow it, and which depend on both the premise set and the additional assumption, are indented (as was the case with the conditional method of proof). The conclusion, since it is the conclusion of the argument proper, is outside the scope of the assumption, i.e., it can be derived from the premise set without the additional assumption (as is evident from our previous justification of the method of indirect proof), and is accordingly not indented. The reason given for the assumption is "Assump (IP)", which means "assumption justified by the indirect method of proof." We do not write after this what is now to be concluded, as we did in the conditional method of proof, for what is now to be proved is the conclusion of the original argument, which has already been stated in our proof. The crucial part of the proof occurs in statements 13 and 14, which contradict one another. One must always derive a contradiction in an indirect proof of validity. To one half of the contradiction one must then, by A_{12}, add the conclusion of the argument; and then by A_4, using the other half of the contradiction, deduce the desired conclusion.

A formal proof of the validity of the argument of Example 92 can be constructed; however, it is much easier to construct an indirect proof of its validity. The ambitious reader will profit greatly if he succeeds in constructing such a formal proof. Let him be cautioned, however, that a formal proof of the validity of this argument, while indeed possible within the framework of the logic we have thus far developed, requires considerable insight into the proper techniques required.

Because the derivation of a contradiction is crucial in the indirect method of proving validity, this method is sometimes called "the *reductio ad absurdum* method". We shall avoid calling it this, however, since we have already applied that appellation to a variant of the truth table method (as is frequently done). Accordingly, when we later refer to the *reductio ad absurdum* method, we shall always mean the variant of the truth table method.

We wish now to examine another English argument, in whose proof of validity we may use both the conditional and the indirect methods. Since the indirect method is a species of the conditional method, it should not surprise us that they can both be used in the same proof of validity. The argument whose validity we wish to prove by the use of both methods follows:

EXAMPLE 94

> The following is not the case; namely, both that Arthur doesn't live on
> Quincy Street and/or owns a tuxedo, and that he both will go down-
> town and not get a ride. Therefore, if Arthur both owns a tuxedo and
> goes downtown, then he will get a ride.   (Q, T, D, R)

A proof of the validity of this argument follows:

EXAMPLE 95

	$/ \therefore (T \cdot D) \supset R$
1. $\sim[(\sim Q \vee T) \cdot (D \cdot \sim R)]$	Pr.
2. $T \cdot D$	Assump $/ \therefore R$
3. $\sim R$	Assump (IP)
4. $\sim[(\sim Q \vee T) \cdot \sim \sim (D \cdot \sim R)]$	1, S(DN)
5. $(\sim Q \vee T) \supset \sim (D \cdot \sim R)$	4, D_{II}
6. D	2, A_8; A_7
7. $D \cdot \sim R$	6, 3, A_9
8. $\sim \sim (D \cdot \sim R)$	7, A_{10}
9. $\sim (\sim Q \vee T)$	5, 8, A_2
10. $\sim \sim (\sim \sim Q \cdot \sim T)$	9, S(D_I)
11. $\sim \sim Q \cdot \sim T$	10, A_{11}
12. $\sim T$	11, A_8; A_7
13. T	2, A_7
14. $T \vee R$	13, A_{12}
15. R	14, 12, A_4
16. $\therefore (T \cdot D) \supset R$	2-15, CP

In this proof, statement 2 is indented, since it marks the beginning of the employment of the conditional method of proof. But,
to derive the conclusion now desired after the assumption of statement 2, the indirect method is invoked. Accordingly, statement 3,
which marks the beginning of the indirect method of proof, and
every statement following it which is derived from it and the premise of the argument (plus the assumption of statement 2), are
indented farther than is statement 2. Statements 12 and 13 reveal
the contradiction which must be established when the indirect
method of proving validity is used. Statement 15 is indented only
as far as was statement 2 since it can be derived from 1 and 2 (as
is evident from our justification of the indirect method); and statement 16 is not indented at all since it can be derived directly from

the premise (as is evident from our justification of the conditional method).

Exercises

GROUP A

451. Explain why the indirect method of proving validity is justified.
452. How is the indirect method related to the conditional method of proving validity?
453. Why cannot the method of indirect proof be used to prove invalidity?
454. For the argument of Example 94, construct a formal proof of validity, a conditional proof which does not use the indirect method, and an indirect proof which does not use the conditional method.
455. Following is a list of numbers of exercises from §29. You have already constructed formal proofs for the validity of the arguments of these exercises. Now construct an indirect proof (without using the conditional method) of the validity of each:

> 426
> 429
> 433
> 437
> 440

GROUP B

For each of the following arguments, construct the kind or kinds of proof of validity indicated in square brackets at the beginning of each exercise. "FP" indicates that a formal proof is required; "CP", a conditional proof without use of the indirect method; "CP & IP", a conditional proof which utilizes the indirect method; and "IP", an indirect proof which does not utilize the conditional method.

456. [FP, IP] The moon is a satellite of the earth, and/or if men travel to it they will never return. Men will travel to the moon and return. Hence the moon is a satellite of the earth. (S, T, R)
457. [FP, IP] The following is not the case; namely, that men traveling to the moon is a necessary condition for their reaching the moon, only if their inhabiting it is a sufficient condition for them to prefer it to the earth. Therefore, if men reach the moon, they will inhabit it. (T, R, I, P)
458. [FP, CP & IP, CP, IP] If men travel to the planet Venus, then they seek adventure and/or profit. If men remain on earth, they are conservatives

even though they seek adventure. Men travel to the planet Venus and/or they remain on earth. Hence, men seek profit if they do not seek adventure.   (V, A, P, E, C)

459. [FP, CP & IP, CP, IP] If the planet Venus is habitable, we must not ignore the possibility of its use for the expanding population. If we think the population expands slowly, we are overly conservative. The planet Venus is habitable and/or we think the population expands slowly. Hence we are overly conservative if we ignore the possibility of using Venus for the expanding population.   (VH, IP, ES, OC)

460. [FP, IP] If Vasco da Gama visited China and Babylon, then he visited Russia and/or Siberia. He visited Russia and/or Siberia only if he did not visit China. If it is not the case that he was an amateur interested in Greece, then it is not the case that he did not visit China and/or was not interested in Greece. He was not an amateur. Hence Vasco da Gama did not visit Babylon.   (C, B, R, S, A, G)

CHAPTER FIVE

Quantification

§32. Predicate-Subject Notation and Universal Quantification

When we were talking about our functionally complete set of operators, $\{ \cdot, \sim \}$, earlier, we made the qualification that this set is functionally complete with regard only to statements *of the types thus far considered.* Very well, what other types of statements have not thus far been considered? An instance of one new type appears in the first premise of the following argument:

EXAMPLE 96

Anybody who has a fever is ill. Jane has a fever. Therefore Jane is ill.

This argument is not a simple instance of A_1, for the first statement cannot be translated into the standard $P \supset Q$ form. Nonetheless, the argument is obviously valid. If the first premise can be reworded to involve an "if · · · then—" form, we may be able to prove its validity by the use of A_1, although perhaps another valid argument form may also have to be introduced.

Accordingly, let us examine the meaning of the first premise of this argument. When we say "Anybody who has a fever is ill", we mean it is true of anybody, not just Jane, or the man next door who wonders about the muscle-building virtues of spinach, that if he has a fever, then he is ill. This analysis indicates that we are on the right track if we wish to restate the first premise of our argument so that it includes an "if · · · then—" statement. For we can now restate it as follows:

It is true of anybody that: if he has a fever, then he is ill.

This formulation of the statement suggests that, if we are to translate it symbolically, we shall have to introduce a new notation to take care of the first part of the statement, i.e., the "it is true of anybody that" part.

Before we entertain this task, however, let us look at the second half of the statement in our new formulation, namely, the "if he has a fever, then he is ill" part.

Will it suffice merely to translate this second part of the statement by means of the standard $P \supset Q$ form? Presuming we could extricate this part of the statement by means of some new valid argument form, here is what would result:

EXAMPLE 97

    If he has a fever, then he is ill. Jane has a fever. Therefore Jane is ill.

If we translate "He has a fever" by HF, "He is ill" by HI, "Jane has a fever" by JF, and "Jane is ill" by JI, we would get:

EXAMPLE 98

    HF $\supset$ HI
    JF
    $\therefore$ JI

This is most certainly *not* an instance of A_1. But let us look separately at the four atomic statements involved in Example 97:

    1. He has a fever.
    2. He is ill.
    3. Jane has a fever.
    4. Jane is ill.

While according to our previous mode of translating statements like this, these statements are treated as four entirely distinct atomic statements, there nevertheless are some rather obvious relationships obtaining among them. Specifically, statements 1 and 2 have the same subject ("he"), and so do statements 3 and 4 ("Jane"); further, statements 1 and 3 have the same predicate ("has a fever"), and so do statements 2 and 4 ("is ill"). We can introduce a new type of notation which will make these relationships evident.

Let us translate the *predicate* of a statement by a single capital letter (such as F for "has a fever", and I for "is ill"), and let us translate the *subject* of a statement by a single lower case subscript following the capital letter which we use to translate the *predicate* (such as $_x$ for the ambiguous pronoun "he", and $_j$ for "Jane"). Thus, the four atomic statements of our argument can be translated into symbolic notation, respectively, as follows:

    1. F_x 2. I_x 3. F_j 4. I_j

Then Example 97 (which still omits the first part of the first premise of our original argument) can be translated into symbolic notation as follows:

$$F_x \supset I_x$$
$$F_j$$
$$\therefore I_j$$

This is not yet of the form A_1; but at least there are now evident relationships among the statements of the argument, much resembling those that we would expect in a simple instance of A_1.

Before we can legitimately establish a proof of the validity of our original argument (Example 96), we must go back and pick up what has been neglected of our first premise, namely, the "it is true of anybody that" part. Our analysis of this first premise has progressed to the point where we can partially translate it into symbolic notation, thus:

It is true of anybody that: $(F_x \supset I_x)$

Let us begin our analysis of the first part of this statement by observing that our translation of it should have some notational resemblance to the translation of the second part. Specifically, the $_x$ should be mentioned. What we wish to say is that the statement $F_x \supset I_x$ is true of any x. Or, in other words:

For any x: $(F_x \supset I_x)$

Now let us simply translate this "for any x" by an x placed in parentheses in front of the hypothetical conditional statement, thus:

$$(x)(F_x \supset I_x)$$

What is the logical status of this new expression, (x)? It is a logical operator, of the same status as our other operators like $\cdot$ and $\sim$. It is, however, a new operator which *cannot* be defined in terms of $\cdot$ and $\sim$. Our functionally complete set will accordingly have to be expanded.

Let us elaborate a bit on what we have established thus far in this section. Four things have emerged:

1. A new type of symbolic translation of statements which indicates both their predicates and their subjects.
2. A new logical operator, (x).
3. The necessity of expanding our set of operators, $\{ \cdot, \sim \}$, to make the set functionally complete for our new type of statement.
4. A suggestion that a new valid argument form shall have to be introduced to enable us to prove the validity of arguments such as the one we have considered in this section.

Some remarks will be made about each of these four topics, in order.

First, as for the new type of symbolic translation of statements which indicates both their predicates and their subjects: The general form for such statements shall be written Φ_α, using the Greek letter Φ (*phi*), to represent the predicate of any statement, and the Greek letter α (*alpha*) to designate any subject. Φ_α designates all expressions written in predicate-subject notation, including the general "if $\cdots$ then—" form, in terms of the predicate-subject notation, namely, $\varphi_z \supset \psi_x$. Here, the Greek letter ψ (*psi*) is used to indicate a second predicate sign. Here, too, we use x's rather than α's. We are reserving the expression Φ_α to designate any expression in terms of our predicate-subject notation. Φ_α merely expresses the fact that something may be said of something else, such as that if it has a fever it is ill, or, in the general form, $\varphi_x \supset \psi_x$. Φ_α can then be used to designate all the various expressions $\varphi_x \supset \psi_x, \varphi_y \supset \psi_y, \varphi_z \supset \psi_z$, etc.

Specific instances of the general "if $\cdots$ then—" form in our new notation (i.e., of $\varphi_x \supset \psi_x$) will be notated with appropriate letters chosen to represent the specific English statements concerned. Thus, we translate "If Jane has a fever, then Jane is ill" by $F_j \supset I_j$. In this instance, both atomic statements have the same subject. If the subjects differ, the general form for the hypothetical conditional would be $\varphi_x \supset \psi_y$, wherein two different letters, $_x$ and $_y$, are used to indicate two different subjects. An instance of this general form is "If Jane has a fever, then Grace will be concerned", symbolized as $F_j \supset C_g$, which uses two different letters, $_j$ and $_g$, to indicate the two different subjects, "Jane" and "Grace", respectively.

So much for the new predicate-subject notation. Let us pass now to a consideration of the second item we have introduced in this section, namely the new logical operator, (x).

This operator is sometimes called "the *all-operator*", because it indicates that the statement which follows it holds for *all* members of the universe of discourse. Thus, (x) may be read, "for *all* x", as well as "for *any* x".

More frequently, however, logicians refer to this operator as "the *universal quantifier*", because it tells us that the statement which follows it is true for a specified *quantity* of members of the class being considered, namely, the *universal* quantity, which is the same as saying that the given statement is true *for all x*. The quantifier (y) could as well be used, in which case the statement which followed it would be said to be true *for all y*. And so forth, with (z), etc.

The general form of a statement of the hypothetical conditional form, $\varphi_x \supset \psi_x$, and preceded by the universal quantifier, is $(x)(\varphi_x \supset \psi_x)$, which may be read "for all x, if φ may be predicated of x, then ψ may be predicated of x", or "for all x, if φ is a property of x, then ψ is a property of x", or "for all x, if φ of x, then ψ of x". (And instead of "for all x", we may say "for any x".) A statement, such as one of this form, preceded by the universal quantifier, is called "a *universally quantified statement*".

Statements involving the words "all", "any", "each", and the like, are universally quantified statements because they indicate that what is said is true of all members of the universe of discourse. Such statements should be translated into symbolic notation with the aid of the universal quantifier. Thus a statement like "All snow is white" would be translated into symbolic notation as $(x)(S_x \supset W_x)$, that is to say, "for any x, if x is snow, then x is white."

Furthermore, statements of the form "no A's are B", are translated with the aid of the universal quantifier, for they assert that, for all A's, B can *not* be predicated of them. Thus, "No crows are white" would be translated symbolically as $(x)(C_x \supset \sim W_x)$, meaning "for any x, if x is a crow, then x is not white." This means the same thing as the English statement "All crows are not white", for it asserts, of all crows, that they are not white; or "for any x, if x is a crow, then x is not white."

Note that while "All crows are not white" makes an affirmative assertion about all crows, to the effect that they are not white, the statement "Not all crows are white", is quite a different type of statement, for it denies that is true of the class of all x's that if x is a crow, then x is white. The statement "Not all crows are white", would be translated symbolically as follows: $\sim(x)(C_x \supset W_x)$.

Let us be extremely careful to make this distinction between statements of the forms "All A's are not B" and "Not all A's are B". If we say "All A's are not B", this means that none of them are; whereas "Not all A's are B" does allow the possibility that *some* A's may be B. Thus, the statement "All swans are not white" means that there are not any swans which are white; whereas "Not all swans are white" merely means that some of them are not white, thus allowing the possibility that perhaps some *are* white. But of course this possibility is just a possibility; and it would be illegitimate to make a positive inference from the statement "Not all swans are white" to the statement "Some swans are white." Just so, were we told that not all philosophers have three green heads with two purple horns on each (which is true), we should understand from this information simply that there are some philosophers who do not fit this description. We could not legitimately infer thereby (no matter what our personal opinion of philosophers) that there are some philosophers who actually *do* fit this description.

It should be noted, further, that statements of the form "All A's are B" are hypothetical conditionals. They merely assert, for example, that for any x, *if* x is a unicorn, *then* x has a horn, without asserting the existence of unicorns. It would be incorrect to translate such statements as conjunctions, thus: "For any x, x is a unicorn *and* x has a horn." This statement would mean that everything under the sun, and in fact including the sun, is a unicorn with a horn! For after all, the sun too, as well as everything under it, is an x; which indicates that the class of all x's is the class of everything in the universe. To be sure, since the statement "All unicorns have horns" is true, even the sun would have a horn if it were a unicorn. But since the symbolic formulation of the statement "All unicorns have horns" remains *hypothetical,* we shall not be led to the monstrous conclusion that everything in the universe is a horned unicorn. The moral of all this is that statements of the form "All A's are B" are translated symbolically as hypothetical conditionals.

We have used the device of referring to statements of the "All A's

are B" type, rather than to universally quantified statements, for a
specific reason. Not all universally quantified statements are of the
"All A's are B" type, and hence not necessarily hypothetical in their
symbolic formulation. Thus, there is no hypothetical conditional involved in a statement of the form $(x)\varphi_x$. Or consider a statement such
as "Everything is either animate or inanimate." This plainly is a disjunctive statement. Nevertheless, the moral remains: statements of
the form "All A's are B" are translated into symbolic notation as
hypothetical conditionals. And this goes for all forms reducible to
the "All A's are B" type, such as "No A's are B", "Everything that
is an A is a B", etc.

Two observations shall here be made concerning notational conventions. The first observation has to do with enclosing in parentheses the expression which follows the quantifier, thus: $(x)(\varphi_x \supset
\psi_x)$. Why do we not write this simply as $(x)\varphi_x \supset \psi_x$? For, after all,
when only one predicate-subject sign (such as φ_x) follows the universal quantifier, it is not put in parentheses: $(x)\varphi_x$. We shall answer
this question by means of an analogy. When an atomic statement is
negated, we write $\sim P$, without enclosing the P in parentheses. We
could write $\sim(P)$, but since $\sim P$ is unambiguous, we omit the parentheses. However, when a molecular statement is negated, it is placed
in parentheses, thus: $\sim(P \supset Q)$. The universal quantifier is an operator just like the $\sim$, and like it, indicates that everything which
follows it is covered by it. So, just as $\sim(P \supset Q)$ and $\sim P \supset Q$ mean
two entirely different things, so do $(x)(\varphi_x \supset \psi_x)$ and $(x)\varphi_x \supset \psi_x$. In the
last expression, the ψ_x is not quantified. In the expression $(x)(\varphi_x \supset
\psi_x)$, both the $_x$ after the φ and the $_x$ after the ψ are said to be within
the *scope* of the quantifier, and are therefore said to be *bound variables*.
In the expression $(x)\varphi_x \supset \psi_x$, however, although the $_x$ after the φ is
bound, i.e., is within the *scope* of the quantifier, the last $_x$ is *not* within
the quantifier's scope, and is therefore said to be a *free variable*. As for
the x in the quantifier, it is said to be *bound*.

The other observation with regard to notational convention is this:
A tilde before a quantified statement negates the entire statement.
Hence, a negative quantified statement could, strictly, be written as
an instance of this form: $\sim[(x)(\varphi_x \supset \psi_x)]$. We shall omit the square
brackets, however, and write the statement simply as an instance of
the following form: $\sim(x)(\varphi_x \supset \psi_x)$. Some students mistakenly think

that, when a statement is written as an instance of this form, without the square brackets, only the quantifier, and not the statement which follows it, is negated. This makes no sense; for logical operators cannot be negated (and (x) is, after all, a logical operator); only statements can be negated.

Let us pass now to a consideration of the third major point of this section, namely, the expansion of our set of operators, $\{\cdot, \sim\}$, to make the set functionally complete for our new type of statement. We have already said that (x) cannot be defined in terms of $\{\cdot, \sim\}$. An obvious thing to do then would appear simply to be to add (x) to our functionally complete set. But we also mentioned that in addition to the class of all x's, we could talk about the class of all y's, or z's, in which case we would use the operators (y) and (z). Does this mean we must also include these in our functionally complete set, in addition to (x)? We can provide for a diversity of universal quantifiers if we merely add (α) to our set, using the Greek letter, α, enclosed in parentheses, to stand for *all* universal quantifiers.

Perhaps a question presents itself to the reader at this point. We previously said that the class of all x's was the class of everything in the universe. Why, then, would we ever use the quantifiers (y) or (z), etc., since they would apply to the same universe of discourse as does the quantifier (x)? We can answer this by considering a linguistic example:

Everyone's father is a man.

This is interpreted to mean: "For every x, and for every y, if y is the father of x, then y is a man." It would be translated with the use of two quantifiers (x) and (y), because it is here necessary to refer to all individuals as x's for one purpose (i.e., the consideration that each *may have* a father), and as y's for another purpose (i.e., the consideration that each *may be* a father). Otherwise, if we used just (x), our translation would have the embarrassing consequence that everyone is his own father.

The immediate consequence of being able to refer to any individual as an x, or a y, etc., is that we must either list all possible universal quantifiers (x), (y), (z), etc., in our functionally complete set of operators, or else include just the symbol (α) to designate all of these universal quantifiers. We may introduce (α) to cover them all, since they all cover the same thing, namely everything in the universe. Accordingly, the set of logical operators which we shall now call functionally complete (again with the qualification that it is functionally complete for statements of the types thus far considered, since it would have to be expanded further if we were to extend our logic further than we shall in this book) is the following set: $\{ \cdot, \sim, (\alpha) \}$.

So much for the third of the four major points of this section. The fourth is merely the suggestion that a new valid argument form is needed to enable us to establish the validity of arguments involving quantified statements. So far, we know how to translate into completely symbolic notation an argument like that at the beginning of this section, namely:

> If anyone has a fever, then he is ill. Jane has a fever. Therefore Jane is ill.

Yet, even knowing how to translate these statements, we cannot construct a formal proof of the validity of this argument, since none of the valid argument forms, A_1 through A_{12}, nor the definitions and other principles used in the construction of formal proofs of validity, apply to quantified statements. A new argument form will have to be introduced before we can prove the validity of this argument. This new form will be the subject of the following section. In successive sections we shall encounter additional argument forms to enable us to construct formal proofs of the validity of various other types of arguments involving quantified statements.

EXERCISES

GROUP A

461. What is the logical status of (x)?
462. Why are statements of the "All A's are B" variety translated symbolically as hypothetical conditionals?
463. Explain the difference in meaning of the statements "All crows are not black" and "Not all crows are black."
464. Explain the difference in meaning of $(x)(\varphi_x \supset \psi_x)$ and $(x)\varphi_x \supset \psi_x$.
465. What is meant by the *scope* of a quantifier?
466. What is a free variable?
467. What is a bound variable?

468. Why is (α) introduced into our functionally complete set of operators rather than (x)?

469. In a universally quantified statement, is the x in the quantifier bound or free?

470. Why will we have to introduce at least one new valid argument form?

GROUP B

Translate the following statements into predicate-subject notation, using the suggested symbols.

Sample: Grace has a fever and Jane is ill. (F, I; $_{g, j}$)
Answer: $F_g \cdot I_j$

471. Snow is white. (W; $_s$)
472. Grass is green and snow is white. (G, W; $_{g, s}$)
473. Snow is white and cotton is white; whereas grass is green. (W, G; $_{s, c, g}$)
474. If Socrates is human, then Socrates is mortal. (H, M; $_s$)
475. x is a crow and x is black. (C, B; $_x$)
476. If x has a fever, then x is ill. (F, I; $_x$)
477. If x is a crow, then x is black. (C, B; $_x$)
478. If Tabby is a cat, then Tabby has fur. (C, F; $_t$)
479. Tabby is a cat, and Tabby has fur. (C, F; $_t$)
480. Arthur proposed and Grace accepted. (P, A; $_{a, g}$)

GROUP C

Using the predicate-subject notation, translate the following universally quantified statements. The letters by which you are to designate the predicates are suggested in parentheses. Use the universal quantifier (x); and use $_x$ throughout to indicate the subjects.

Sample Exercises:

a. All snow is white. (S, W)
Answer: $(x)(S_x \supset W_x)$ [That is to say, "For any x, if x is snow, then x is white."]

b. Not all swans are white. (S, W)
Answer: $\sim(x)(S_x \supset W_x)$ [That is to say, "It is not the case that, for any x, if x is a swan, then x is white."]

c. All crows are not white. (C, W)
Answer: $(x)(C_x \supset \sim W_x)$ [That is to say, "For any x, if x is a crow, then x is not white."]

d. No crows are white.

Answer: (x)($C_x \supset \sim W_x$) [This means the same as sample exercise c.]

Translate the following statements in the same manner:

481. All is not lost.   (L)
482. Not all is lost.   (L)
483. Nothing is lost.   (L)
484. Everything is lost.   (L)
485. All men aren't color-blind.   (M, C)
486. Not all men are color-blind.   (M, C)
487. No men are color-blind.   (M, C)
488. No men aren't color-blind.   (M, C)
489. All humans are mortal.   (H, M)
490. No humans are mortal.   (H, M)
491. All cities are not named "Reno".   (C, R)
492. Not all cities are named "Reno".   (C, R)
493. No city is named "Reno".   (C, R)
494. All cities are named "Reno".   (C, R)
495. Every city is named "Reno".   (C, R)
496. Every city is not named "Reno".   (C, R)
497. Not every city is named "Reno".   (C, R)
498. Not every city is not named "Reno".   (C, R)
499. Every man is deaf.   (M, D)
500. Not every man is deaf.   (M, D)
501. Not every man is not deaf.   (M, D)
502. Each man is not deaf.   (M, D)
503. No men are deaf.   (M, D)
504. No men aren't deaf.   (M, D)
505. It isn't true that if anyone proposes marriage to Jane he will receive a favorable reply.   (P, R)

§33.   Universal Instantiation

We are now able to translate, into completely symbolic form, arguments such as the following:

EXAMPLE   99

If anyone has a fever, then he is ill. Jane has a fever. Therefore, Jane is ill.

As we have shown, this argument may be symbolically translated as follows:

EXAMPLE   100

$(x)(F_x \supset I_x)$
F_j
$\therefore I_j$

We have also indicated that another valid argument form must be introduced in order to enable us to prove the validity of arguments such as this one. Let us explain just what would be involved in the new argument form which is required.

The first premise of the argument under consideration says that $F_x \supset I_x$ is true *for all x.* Now, if $F_x \supset I_x$ is true *for all x,* i.e., for *all* members of the universal class, then it is true for *any* member which we may select of this class. Let us use the notation x* to indicate *any* member of this class. Or, if we are using y or z instead of x, then we may designate *any* member of the class by y* or by z*. Then, what we wish to assert is the following valid argument form:

A_{13}: $(\alpha)\Phi_\alpha$
$\therefore \Phi_\alpha{}^*$

The α^* designates x*, y*, z*, etc., for our general formulation of this new argument form, A_{13}. The asterisk, *, indicates that the individual designated by the use of the asterisk is an ambiguous or a specific individual which is representative of the entire class of individuals. We might not wish to name the individual, in which case we would retain the ambiguity by using the asterisk. Thus, if we are told that *all* crows are black, we may wish to conclude, of *any* crow, that it is black, without specifying that it must be the crow I saw at 7:03 this morning on the twelfth limb from the ground in the shade tree outside my window, rather than some other crow.

Yet there are times when we may wish to specify *exactly* which individual of the class we are talking about. Thus, to prove the validity of the argument of Example 99, we wish to talk not about an ambiguous individual, but rather about the very specific individual, *Jane.* Therefore we shall apply our new valid argument form, A_{13}, by choosing *Jane* as the representative individual of the universal class. Accordingly, our proof for the validity of this argument would begin as follows:

$$\diagup \therefore I_j$$

1. $(x)(F_x \supset I_x)$ Pr.

2. F_j Pr.
3. $F_j \supset I_j$ 1, A_{13}

Now it is a simple matter to complete this proof by applying A_1 to statements 3 and 2, thus:

4. $\therefore I_j$ 3, 2, A_1

Note that in the general formulation of A_{13}, no hypothetical conditional appears, although when we used this form in the preceding proof of validity, there was a hypothetical conditional statement. But let us consider what is meant by $(\alpha)\Phi_\alpha$. This simply means that *something* (here designated by Φ) is true of everything. The first premise of our argument, $(x)(F_x \supset I_x)$, also says that *something* (here specified by $F_x \supset I_x$) is true of everything. Thus $(x)(F_x \supset I_x)$ is a legitimate instance of the general form $(\alpha)\Phi_\alpha$.

A_{13} states, essentially, that what is true of all members of the universal class is true of any *instance* (i.e., any member) of that class. For this reason, logicians generally refer to this new valid argument form as "the *Principle of Universal Instantiation*". In order to use the valid argument forms which we previously established, when universally quantified statements are involved, A_{13} is necessasy so that we may be able to work with unquantified instances of the universal statements.

EXERCISES

GROUP A

506. Explain why A_{13} is justified.
507. What is the technical name for A_{13}? Explain the name.
508. What is the significance of the asterisk in our formulation of A_{13}?
509. Why does no asterisk appear in our proof of the validity of the argument of Example 99?
510. Why did we not state A_{13} as follows:

$$(x)\Phi_x$$
$$\therefore \Phi_x *$$

GROUP B

Using the suggested notation, construct a formal proof of the validity of each of the following arguments:

511. All humans are mortal. Socrates is human. Therefore Socrates is mortal. (H, M; $_{x, s}$)

512. If anybody disagrees with the organization, he will be sorry. Andrews disagrees with the organization. Therefore Andrews will be sorry. (D, S; $_{x, a}$)

513. Everybody who is bald uses our new Natur-Hair-Remedy. All who use our new Natur-Hair-Remedy are satisfied. Andrews is bald. Hence Andrews is satisfied. (B, N, S; $_{x, a}$)

514. Everybody who is bald uses our new Natur-Hair-Remedy; and all who use our new Natur-Hair-Remedy are satisfied. However, Jones is not satisfied. Hence Jones is not bald. (B, N, S; $_{x, j}$)

515. Everybody who is bald uses our new Natur-Hair-Remedy. Anybody who is really sensible doesn't use our new Natur-Hair-Remedy. Bradley is bald. Hence Bradley is not really sensible. (B, N, S; $_{x, b}$)

516. All peacocks strut whenever they mate. Alfonse, whom I saw in the zoo, is a mating peacock. Therefore Alfonse struts. (P, S, M; $_{x, a}$)

517. All the doors in this house are white if they are not black. No newly painted door in this house is black. The door to this room is newly painted. Hence, the door to this room is white. (D, W, B, P; $_{x, r}$)

518. No brand of crouton is good if it becomes soggy. Any brand of crouton which is not good is prohibited in this restaurant. Mother Martha Brand croutons become soggy. Therefore Mother Martha Brand croutons are prohibited in this restaurant. (B, S, G, P; $_{x, m}$)

519. All men with niphablepsia should wear dark glasses and avoid snow in the daytime. Jones is a man with niphablepsia. Therefore Jones should avoid snow in the daytime and should wear dark glasses. (M, N, G, S; $_{x, j}$)

520. All persons with atherosclerosis have an excess of cholesterol in their veins. All persons with an excess of cholesterol in their veins should limit their intake of saturated fatty acids. Jones is a person with atherosclerosis. Hence Jones should limit his intake of saturated fatty acids. (P, A, C, F; $_{x, j}$)

§34. Universal Generalization

Suppose we encounter an argument, involving universally quantified statements, such as the following:

EXAMPLE 101

If anyone has a fever, then he is ill. If anyone is ill, he should see a physician. Hence, if anyone has a fever, he should see a physician.

A_{13} will not be the only valid argument form involving universally quantified statements which will be necessary in the proof of the validity of this argument. For the conclusion of A_{13} is *not* quantified, whereas the conclusion of the argument of Example 101 *is* quantified. We shall need, then, another valid argument form whose conclusion is in the form of a universally quantified statement.

Let us begin the proof for the validity of the argument of Example 101, and see how far we can get with just the thirteen valid argument forms that we know. Then we shall be able to see exactly what will be required by our new form. The predicates of the statements of Example 101 we shall translate by F, I, and P, respectively. Our proof, then, would begin as follows:

$$\diagup \therefore (x)(F_x \supset P_x)$$

1.	$(x)(F_x \supset I_x)$	Pr.
2.	$(x)(I_x \supset P_x)$	Pr.
3.	$F_x{}^* \supset I_x{}^*$	1, A_{13}
4.	$I_x{}^* \supset P_x{}^*$	2, A_{13}
5.	$F_x{}^* \supset P_x{}^*$	3, 4, A_3

Here we have instantiated the two premises, by A_{13}, and used the resulting two instantiations, with A_3, to get statement 5. We chose the ambiguous individual, x^*, in our instantiation of premise 2 as well as in our instantiation of premise 1 (rather than choosing another individual, such as x^{**}, in our instantiation of premise 2), so that we would be talking about the same individual when we used A_3 later. Uniform replacement for P and Q in A_3 demands that exactly the same individual be used; otherwise $I_x{}^*$ would replace Q in the first premise of A_3, and $I_x{}^{**}$ would replace Q in the second premise of A_3.

Thus far, then, our proof is correct. But now, from $F_x{}^* \supset P_x{}^*$, which is *not* a universally quantified statement, we must conclude $(x)(F_x \supset P_x)$, which *is* a universally quantified statement. A new valid argument form must be introduced at this point to enable us to draw the desired conclusion for the argument under consideration.

Let us look at the nature of this inference, from $F_x{}^* \supset P_x{}^*$ to $(x)(F_x \supset P_x)$, which is required in our proof of validity. The individual, x^*, is an ambiguous individual, which is representative of the class of all x's. Now, if something is true of *any* representative individual which we may select from this class, it is true of *all* members of the class. This is the principle which we wish to formulate into our new valid argument form. We shall do this in the following manner:

$$A_{14}: \quad \Phi_\alpha{}^*$$
$$\therefore (\alpha)\Phi_\alpha$$

This form is exactly what we need to prove the argument of Example 101 valid. It says that if something (Φ) is true of *any* individual which we might select, then it is true of *all* individuals. The α^* might not refer to an ambiguous individual, but rather to a specific individual which is nevertheless representative of the universal class.

We can now complete our proof of the validity of the argument of Example 101 as follows:

6. $\therefore (x)(F_x \supset P_x)$ 5, A_{14}

Logicians call this new valid argument form which we have introduced, "the *Principle of Universal Generalization*". That the name is apt is obvious from the fact that the new form *generalizes* to a *universal* statement. In other words, it states that if something is true of *any* individual, then we can *universally generalize* and say that it is true of *all* individuals.

It is important to observe that, in our formulation of A_{14}, α^* indicates an individual which is *representative* of the universal class. Accordingly, when we generalize in a proof of validity, we must be sure that the individual from which we generalize is one which is *representative* of the entire class. Thus we could *not* conclude, from the knowledge that Jane has a fever, that everybody has a fever. This would represent an illegitimate application of A_{14}, since Jane's abnormal body temperature would not be representative of that of everything in the universe. Of course, if the individual from which we generalize is an ambiguous or specific individual which we previously got by A_{13}, then we know that it is representative. Such was the case in our proof for the validity of the argument of Example 101.

EXERCISES

GROUP A

521. What is the technical name for A_{14}? Explain the name.

522. Why is it necessary to add A_{14} to our logic?
523. Why is A_{14} justified?
524. What is the significance of the asterisk in the formulation of A_{14}?
525. Why did we not state A_{14} as follows:

$$\Phi_x^*$$
$$\therefore (x)\Phi_x$$

GROUP B

Construct a formal proof of validity for each of the following arguments, using the suggested predicate notation:

526. All humans are mortal. All mortals are rational animals. Therefore all humans are rational animals.   (H, M, R)
527. No humans are completely contented. All students are humans. Therefore no students are completely contented.   (H, C, S)
528. All crows are birds. All birds have wings. Therefore all crows have wings.   (C, B, W)
529. All colds can be cured with vitamin C. Everything that can be cured with vitamin C is the result of a nutritional deficiency. Hence all colds are the result of a nutritional deficiency.   (C, V, D)
530. No one who is not healthy is efficient, whereas everyone who is productive is efficient. Consequently no one who is not healthy is productive.   (H, E, P)
531. No Aristotelian maintains the Platonic World of Ideas. No one who does not maintain the Platonic World of Ideas finds the philosophy of Plotinus congenial. Hence no Aristotelian finds the philosophy of Plotinus congenial.   (A, I, P)
532. No elephants have feathers. Nothing that does not have feathers has wings. Nothing that does not have wings is airborne. Therefore no elephant is airborne.   (E, F, W, A)
533. Anybody with nyctalopia must be cautious if he drives at night. Anyone who must be cautious whenever he drives at night should be under the care of an oculist. Therefore anybody with nyctalopia should be under the care of an oculist.   (N, C, D, O)
534. Anyone who takes placebos is deceived if he thinks he is taking medication. Anyone who is deceived will resent it if he finds out. Hence anyone who takes placebos and thinks he is taking medication, will resent it if he finds out.   (P, D, M, R, F)
535. Any attorney who knows logic will not be deceived in law courts if he is presented with fallacious arguments. Anyone who will not be deceived in law courts if he is presented with fallacious arguments will acquire an

enviable reputation. Hence any attorney who knows logic will acquire an enviable reputation.   (A, L, D, F, R)

§35. Existential Quantification

We have successively proved the validity of arguments involving universally quantified statements, statements in which the words "all", "every", "each", and so forth, appear. But consider the following argument:

EXAMPLE   102

All sparrows are gray. Some birds are sparrows. Therefore some birds are gray.   (S, G, B)

There is no problem about translating the first premise of this argument. The translation is: $(x)(S_x \supset G_x)$.

But what about the second premise and the conclusion? They contain the word "some". Moreover, they are *not* universally quantified statements; for the word "some" indicates that only part of the universal class, and not the whole class, is being talked about. Yet the statements are definitely quantified, for "some" indicates a certain quantity of members.

We have here encountered a new type of quantified statement. Let us analyze it as we did universally quantified statements. The first thing we shall do is try to ascertain just what is meant by a statement like "Some birds are sparrows."

"Some birds are sparrows" means "There are some individuals which are birds and which are sparrows", or, in partially symbolic notation, "There are some x's such that: $B_x \cdot S_x$."

Thus, we see that, like universally quantified statements, this new type of statement consists of two parts. The second part $(B_x \cdot S_x)$ is a standard conjunction. It is the first part ("there are some x's such that") which we must yet translate symbolically.

Let us look at the phrase, "There are some x's such that". What exactly does it mean? It asserts that there is actually existing something such that $\cdots$. Or, there exists at least one x such that $\cdots$. At any rate, the import of the phrase seems to be that the individuals talked about *really* exist. Existence, then, is implied by the phrase.

That this was not the case with regard to universally quantified statements we recall from our previous discussion. We can truly say that all unicorns have horns, but we would never wish to say that there actually are (i.e., exist) any unicorns with horns. Thus, while "All unicorns have horns" is true, "Some unicorns have horns" is false.

Very well, the phrase "there are some x's such that" has existential import. But how many x's does it refer to, i.e., what *quantity* of existing x's is involved? The answer is not "one", or "two", or "three", etc., but simply, "at least one". That is all that "some" means. It implies an indefinite quantity. If only one bird were a sparrow, the assertion that some birds are sparrows would be true. And if exactly one million birds were sparrows, the assertion that some birds are sparrows would still be true. Thus, the phrase "there are some x's such that" means "there exists at least one x such that".

Logicians translate this phrase into symbolic notation thus: $(\exists x)$, using a reverse E with an x after it, and the whole expression enclosed in parentheses. Accordingly, the statement "Some birds are sparrows" is translated symbolically as $(\exists x)(B_x \cdot S_x)$. Statements of this form are called *"existentially quantified statements";* and the $(\exists x)$ is called *"the existential quantifier"* because it asserts existential import. Less frequently, this kind of quantification is called *"particular quantification",* and the $(\exists x)$ is called "the *some operator".*

$(\exists x)$ has the status of a new logical operator, as do $(\exists y)$, $(\exists z)$, etc., if we are designating individuals by y, z, etc., rather than by x. We shall use the notation $(\exists \alpha)$ to designate all of these operators; just as we used (α) to designate (x), (y), (z), etc. However, $(\exists \alpha)$ need not be added to our functionally complete set of operators, $\{\ \cdot,\ \sim,\ (\alpha)\ \}$, for it may be defined in terms of this set, as we shall see in a later section.

As we might suspect, the introduction of the existential quantifier will require the introduction of some new valid argument forms. These shall be considered in the section which immediately follows this one. Right now, however, we shall concentrate on the translation into symbolic form of existentially quantified statements.

Just as there are several ways in which *universally* quantified statements can be formulated in English (by using the words "all", "every", "each", etc.), so there are various ways in which *existentially* quantified statements can be formulated in English.

The most common way of indicating existentially quantified statements in English is by the use of the word "some", as in the statement "Some birds are sparrows." Or sometimes the word "something" is used instead, as in the statements "Something is a bird and a sparrow" and "There is something which is a bird and a sparrow." The phrase "there is" (or "there are") always indicates existential import, as does the equivalent phrase, "there exists" (or "there exist"). Thus logicians generally read $(\exists x)$ as "there is an x such that" or "there exists an x such that". As well, the negative statement beginning "there is not" (or "there are not") is a statement, translated symbolically with a tilde before the existential quantifier, thus: $\sim(\exists x)$.

Note that we translated the statement "Some birds are sparrows" by a *conjunction:* $(\exists x)(B_x \cdot S_x)$. This is because the existentially quantified statement indicates the actual existence of an individual of which two things (here designated by B and S) can be predicated. Since the individual is known to exist, it can be said to possess *both* properties. This will, of course, have to be indicated by the sign for conjunction: $\cdot$. Recall that statements of the form "All A's are B" are translated as hypothetical conditionals, for they do not assert existential import; rather do they assert merely that *if* such-and-such, *then* thus-and-so. The general rule to be observed, then, with regard to compound statements involving quantification, is this:

Translate universally quantified statements as hypothetical conditionals, and existentially quantified statements as conjunctions.

This general rule does not apply, of course, to *universally* quantified statements of forms other than the "All A's are B" type, as we mentioned earlier; nor to such *existentially* quantified statements as those of the form $(\exists x)\varphi_x$, which are plainly neither hypothetical conditionals nor conjunctions.

EXERCISES

Translate the following statements into symbolic form, using the suggested predicate notation:

536. Some swans are black.   (S, B)
537. Some swans aren't black.   (S, B)
538. There aren't some swans which aren't black.   (S, B)

539. There aren't any swans which aren't black.   (S, B)
540. There is a city which is named "Reno".   (C, R)
541. Some cities aren't named "Reno".   (C, R)
542. There aren't any cities which are named "Reno".   (C, R)
543. There aren't any cities which are not named "Reno".   (C, R)
544. It is not the case that there is not at least one city which is named "Reno". (C, R)
545. It is not the case that there is not at least one city which is not named "Reno".   (C, R)
546. Some men are deaf.   (M, D)
547. Some men aren't deaf.   (M, D)
548. It is not the case that some men aren't deaf.   (M, D)
549. It is not the case that there aren't any men who aren't deaf.   (M, D)
550. There aren't any crows which aren't black.   (C, B)

§36.   Existential Instantiation and Existential Generalization

Now that we are able successfully to translate, into completely symbolic form, existentially quantified statements, let us turn our attention to the matter of proving the validity of arguments which involve existentially quantified statements. As an example, let us consider the argument presented in the preceding section, namely:

EXAMPLE   103

All sparrows are gray. Some birds are sparrows. Therefore some birds are gray.   (S, G, B)

Our proof for the validity of this argument will begin as follows:

$$\diagup \therefore (\exists x)(B_x \cdot G_x)$$

1. $(x)(S_x \supset G_x)$ Pr.
2. $(\exists x)(B_x \cdot S_x)$ Pr.

What we must next do is instantiate both premises. We can easily enough instantiate the universally quantified premise by A_{13}, but we need a valid argument form to allow us to instantiate the existentially quantified premise. What we need is the principle known among logicians as "the *Principle of Existential Instantiation*". Here is what is involved in this principle:

An existentially quantified statement tells us that there is at least one individual such that $\cdots$. Thus, $(\exists\alpha)\Phi\alpha$ tells us tnat there is at least one individual such that Φ may be predicated of it. We can, accordingly, select an individual (perhaps the *only* individual, if there is only one such that Φ may be predicated of it), designate it by the ambiguous α^*, or by a specific designation, and talk about it. Thus, the Principle of Existential Instantiation may be formulated as follows:

A_{15}: $(\exists\alpha)\Phi\alpha$ *Restriction:* α^* designates an individual which has not
       $\therefore\Phi\alpha^*$ been previously mentioned in the proof of validity.

Let us explain the restriction which comprises part of the formulation of the Principle of Existential Instantiation. If we did not place this restriction on A_{15}, we could prove that arguments like the following were valid: "Tabby is a white cat. Some dogs are white. All white dogs bark. Hence Tabby barks." Here is how this would be done (by violating the restriction on A_{15}):

$$\diagup \therefore B_t$$

1. $C_t \cdot W_t$	Pr.
2. $(\exists x)(D_x \cdot W_x)$	Pr.
3. $(x)[(D_x \cdot W_x) \supset B_x]$	Pr.
4. $D_t \cdot W_t$	2, A_{15} [*illegitimate*]
5. $(D_t \cdot W_t) \supset B_t$	3, A_{13}
6. $\therefore B_t$	5, 4, A_1

Here, since $_t$ has already been used to designate a cat (in premise 1), we cannot use it to designate a dog. The symbol $_t$ does not, therefore, designate any individual covered by the statement that some dogs are white.

Bearing in mind this restriction which we must place on A_{15}, let us return to our proof of the validity of the argument of Example 103. So far, we have the following:

$$\diagup \therefore (\exists x)(B_x \cdot G_x)$$

1. $(x)(S_x \supset G_x)$	Pr.
2. $(\exists x)(B_x \cdot S_x)$	Pr.

We now have at our disposal the means for instantiating each of these statements. Further, we wish to instantiate in such a way that the same individual (say x*) is chosen as our instance in each case, so that we may combine B_x* (which we get from the second premise) and G_x* (which we get from the first premise), in order to arrive at our desired conclusion. But if we instantiate the universally quantified premise first, then we cannot instantiate the existentially quantified premise with the same individual, because of the restriction on A_{15}. However, there is no such restriction on the instantiation of universally quantified statements. So, if we instantiate the existentially quantified statement first, we can then instantiate the universally quantified statement by choosing the same individual.

The reason that no such restriction is placed on the instantiation of universally quantified statements is that, since they are hypothetical, neither member can be asserted separately. Thus, although it is true that *if* Tabby is a dog, *then* Tabby barks; we do not have to worry about Tabby barking, because we have been told that Tabby is a cat, and not a dog. However, if we were told that "Tabby" was the name of a dog, then we could use $_t$ in our instantiation of the universal statement with no confusion. We are justified in using $_t$ in our instantiation of a universal statement even if it has previously occurred in a proof of validity, because a universal statement is true of *all* members of the universal class. On the other hand, such instantiation from an existential statement is illegitimate, because existential statements are true only for *some* individuals, and we do not know whether $_t$ represents one of these individuals or not.

So, returning to our proof, we shall have to instantiate the existentially quantified premise before we instantiate the universally quantified premise. In fact, let us make it a rule that:

When a universally quantified statement and an existentially quantified statement are both to be instantiated in a proof of validity, the existentially quantified statement must be instantiated first, that the restriction on A_{15} may not be violated.

Accordingly, let us continue our proof of the validity of the argument under consideration:

3. $B_x* \cdot S_x*$ 2, A_{15}
4. $S_x* \supset G_x*$ 1, A_{13}
5. S_x* 3, A_8; A_7
6. G_x* 4, 5, A_1

7. B_x^* 3, A_7
8. $B_x^* \cdot G_x^*$ 7, 6, A_9

The conclusion which we wish to draw from this is $(\exists x)(B_x \cdot G_x)$. Thus, we shall have to generalize from statement 8 of our proof to the desired conclusion. We already have a Principle of Universal Generalization; analogous to it we need a *Principle of Existential Generalization*, thus:

A_{16}: $\Phi\alpha^*$
       $\therefore (\exists\alpha)\Phi\alpha$

Again, the α^* may designate an ambiguous or a specific individual.
Returning to our proof, we can generalize from a statement about the ambiguous individual, x^*, to the following, by A_{16}:

9. $\therefore (\exists x)(B_x \cdot G_x)$ 8, A_{16}

Let us give one more argument whose proof of validity involves both of our new valid argument forms, A_{15} and A_{16}:

EXAMPLE   104

No dogs are cats. Some cats meow. Hence some things which meow aren't dogs.   (D, C, M)

The proof of the validity of this argument follows. Note that the existentially quantified statement is instantiated *before* the universally quantified statement is, in accordance with the restriction on A_{15}.

EXAMPLE   105

$/ \therefore (\exists x)(M_x \cdot \sim D_x)$

1. $(x)(D_x \supset \sim C_x)$ Pr.
2. $(\exists x)(C_x \cdot M_x)$ Pr.
3. $C_x^* \cdot M_x^*$ 2, A_{15}
4. $D_x^* \supset \sim C_x^*$ 1, A_{13}
5. $\sim \sim C_x^*$ 3, A_7; A_{10}
6. $\sim D_x^*$ 4, 5, A_2
7. M_x^* 3, A_8; A_7
8. $M_x^* \cdot \sim D_x^*$ 7, 6, A_9
9. $\therefore (\exists x)(M_x \cdot \sim D_x)$ 8, A_{16}

EXERCISES

GROUP A

551. What are the technical names for A_{15} and A_{16}?
552. Explain why A_{15} is justified.
553. Explain why A_{16} is justified.
554. Explain the necessity of the restriction on A_{15}.
555. Why was not a restriction, similar to that on A_{15}, placed on A_{13}?

GROUP B

Construct a formal proof of validity for each of the following arguments, in each case using the suggested predicate notation:

556. Some gangsters are murderers. Therefore some murderers are gangsters. (G, M)
557. All birds fly. Some birds build nests. Therefore some things which fly build nests. (B, F, N)
558. Every attorney who has studied logic is well equipped to try cases at court. Some attorneys have studied logic. Therefore some attorneys are well equipped to try cases at court. (A, L, C)
559. All cars with low gas mileage are expensive to maintain. Some cars are not expensive to maintain. Hence some cars don't have low gas mileage. (C, G, E)
560. All books with leather bindings are attractive. Some books are not attractive. Hence some books are not bound in leather. (B, L, A)
561. No philosopher is not wise. Some philosophers do not have common sense. Hence some philosophers who are wise do not have common sense. (P, W, S)
562. No theater can show CinemaScope pictures if it does not have a large screen. Some theaters don't have large screens. Hence some theaters can't show CinemaScope pictures. (T, C, S)
563. No one who is careful plays with fire. Some who play with fire get burned. Hence some who aren't careful get burned. (C, F, B)
564. No one who has an adequate supply of vitamin D is not able to assimilate calcium. No one who does not have an adequate supply of vitamin D is completely healthy. Some who are completely healthy are long-lived. Therefore some who are able to assimilate calcium are long-lived. (D, C, H, L)
565. No tree which is evergreen is deciduous. No tree which is not evergreen does not shed its leaves in the winter. Some trees are deciduous. Hence some trees shed their leaves in the winter. (T, E, D, L)

§37.   Definition of $(\exists\alpha)S$

We have already said that $(\exists\alpha)$ need not be added to our function-ally complete set of operators, because it can be defined in terms of $\{\cdot, \sim, (\alpha)\}$. Let us now see how such a definition is possible.

Consider any statement S and suppose the existential quantifier be-fore it, thus: $(\exists\alpha)S$, which we may read "There is an α such that S." A little reflection will reveal that this is equivalent to the expressions "It is not the case that for all α, not-S" and "It isn't true that for all α, S is not the case." These expressions may be symbolized $\sim(\alpha)\sim S$. We have thus established a way of saying what is meant by $(\exists\alpha)S$, in terms of our functionally complete set of operators. Therefore we can introduce a definition of the existential quantifier as follows:

Definition V: $(\exists\alpha)S =_{df} \sim(\alpha)\sim S$

It is a matter of convention that we include (α) in our functionally complete set of operators, and define $(\exists\alpha)$ in terms of it. We could just as well have taken $(\exists\alpha)$ as primitive, in which case $(\alpha)S$ would be defined as $\sim(\exists\alpha)\sim S$; i.e., "for all α, S" would be definitionally equivalent to "It is not the case that for some α, S is not the case." We shall, however, regard (α) as primitive, defining $(\exists\alpha)$ in terms of the functionally complete set of operators, $\{\cdot, \sim, (\alpha)\}$, by Definition V.

Let us now investigate the practical implications of this definition. Consider an existentially quantified statement, such as "Some swans are white", which we shall symbolize as $(\exists x)(S_x \cdot W_x)$. Here $(S_x \cdot W_x)$ is an instance of S in Definition V. Applying the definition, then, $(\exists x)(S_x \cdot W_x)$ becomes $\sim(x)\sim(S_x \cdot W_x)$. But since this results in a universally quantified statement which is in the form of a con-junction, and since, as we explained earlier, universally quantified statements are generally formulated as hypothetical conditionals rather than as conjunctions, we shall have to transform this conjunc-tion into a hypothetical conditional. The conjunction, as it stands in our statement, is negated, thus: $\sim(S_x \cdot W_x)$. If we double negate the W_x, thus, $\sim(S_x \cdot \sim \sim W_x)$, we are ready to transform this expression, by Definition II, to the following hypothetical conditional: $(S_x \supset \sim W_x)$. Replacing this for $\sim(S_x \cdot W_x)$ in our universally quantified statement, we get $\sim(x)(S_x \supset \sim W_x)$, which is the desired hypotheti-cal conditional form of our universally quantified statement. Let us summarize this by presenting it in the form of a proof of validity, thus:

EXAMPLE   106

$$/ \therefore \sim(x)(S_x \supset \sim W_x)$$

1. $(\exists x)(S_x \cdot W_x)$ Pr.
2. $\sim(x)\sim(S_x \cdot W_x)$ 1, D_V
3. $\sim(x)\sim(S_x \cdot \sim \sim W_x)$ 2, S(DN)
4. $\therefore \sim(x)(S_x \supset \sim W_x)$ 3, S(D_{II})

Conversely, if we are given $\sim(x)(S_x \supset \sim W_x)$, we may conclude $(\exists x)(S_x \cdot W_x)$, as follows:

EXAMPLE   107

$$/ \therefore (\exists x)(S_x \cdot W_x)$$

1. $\sim(x)(S_x \supset \sim W_x)$ Pr.
2. $\sim(x)\sim(S_x \cdot \sim \sim W_x)$ 1, S(D_{II})
3. $\sim(x)\sim(S_x \cdot W_x)$ 2, S(DN)
4. $\therefore (\exists x)(S_x \cdot W_x)$ 3, D_V

As Examples 106 and 107 indicate, $(\exists x)(S_x \cdot W_x)$ and $\sim(x)(S_x \supset \sim W_x)$ mutually imply one another; that is to say, they are logically equivalent.

Since Definition V defines the existential quantifier in terms of the universal, this enables us to transform any existentially quantified statement into a universally quantified one, and vice versa. The following four equivalences cover all conceivable transformations:

1. $[(\exists \alpha)S] \equiv [\sim(\alpha)\sim S]$
2. $[(\exists \alpha)\sim S] \equiv [\sim(\alpha)S]$
3. $[\sim(\exists \alpha)S] \equiv [(\alpha)\sim S]$
4. $[\sim(\exists \alpha)\sim S] \equiv [(\alpha)S]$

Let us see if in fact these four logical equivalences follow from Definition V. Certainly (1) does, for it expresses the logical equivalence asserted by Definition V. As for (2), $\sim(\alpha)\sim \sim S$ is logically equivalent to $(\exists \alpha)\sim S$ by Definition V. Hence, removing the double negation, we arrive at (2).

As for (3), since $(\exists \alpha)S$ is logically equivalent to $\sim(\alpha)\sim S$ by Definition V, we can substitute these logically equivalent expressions within the larger expression having a tilde before it. Thus, we establish that $\sim(\exists\alpha)S$ is equivalent to $\sim\sim(\alpha)\sim S$, which, when the double negation is removed, becomes $(\alpha)\sim S$.

Similarly, the logical equivalence of (4) is established by substituting the logically equivalent expressions, $(\exists\alpha)\sim S$ and $\sim(\alpha)S$, within the larger expressions having the tilde before them. This gives us the equivalence, $[\sim(\exists\alpha)\sim S] \equiv [\sim\sim(\alpha)S]$, which, when the double negation is removed, becomes (4).

We can make the following general observations about the four logical equivalences which we have just established, namely: To transform an existentially quantified statement into a universally quantified one, or vice versa, change the signs both of the entire statements and of the statements after the quantifier. Thus, to change a statement from an existentially to a universally quantified one, or vice versa, three things must be done:

1. If the quantifier is of the form (α), change it to one of the form $(\exists\alpha)$; if it is of the form $(\exists\alpha)$, change it to a quantifier of the form (α).
2. If there is a tilde before the quantifier, remove it; if there is none, add one.
3. If there is a tilde before the statement following the quantifier, remove it; if not, add one.

These rules apply to statements of the forms $(\exists\alpha)S$ and $(\alpha)S$. Since S is generally of the form $\varphi_x \supset \psi_x$ or $\varphi_x \cdot \psi_x$, in a quantified statement, any tilde which is added before it when transforming it from one type of statement form to another (i.e., from an existentially to a universally quantified statement form, or vice versa), will not be present when S is rewritten as either a conjunction or a hypothetical conditional (whichever is appropriate for the type of quantification involved). Rather, a tilde will appear, in the transformation, before the ψ_x. Or, if there is already a tilde before ψ_x, it will be removed. This is because of the application of Definition II, which is necessary in the transformation, as Examples 106 and 107 illustrated. Thus, $(\exists x)(\varphi_x \cdot \psi_x)$ becomes, when transformed to a universally quantified statement form, $\sim(x)(\varphi_x \supset \sim\psi_x)$, as was shown by the instance in Example 106. We can illustrate this also by means of a diagram, utilizing the logical equivalence, $[(\exists\alpha)S] \equiv [\sim(\alpha)\sim S]$, thus:

[	$(\exists x)$	$(\varphi_x \cdot \psi_x)$	]	$\equiv$	[	$\sim$	(x)	$\sim$	$(\varphi_x \cdot \psi_x)$	]
[	$(\exists \alpha)$	S	]	$\equiv$	[	$\sim$	(α)	$\sim$	S	]

Changing $(\exists x)(\varphi_x \cdot \psi_x)$ to a universally quantified statement form, we arrive, as our diagram shows, at $\sim(x)\sim(\varphi_x \cdot \psi_x)$. But since universally quantified statements are generally stated as hypothetical conditionals rather than as conjunctions, this becomes, by applying Definition II, $\sim(x)(\varphi_x \supset \sim \psi_x)$. Thus, there is no tilde before the final $(\varphi_x \supset \sim \psi_x)$, because of the application of Definition II.

In general, then, the following logical equivalences may be established:

1. $[(\exists x)(\varphi_x \cdot \psi_x)] \equiv [\sim(x)(\varphi_x \supset \sim \psi_x)]$
2. $[(\exists x)(\varphi_x \cdot \sim \psi_x)] \equiv [\sim(x)(\varphi_x \supset \psi_x)]$
3. $[\sim(\exists x)(\varphi_x \cdot \psi_x)] \equiv [(x)(\varphi_x \supset \sim \psi_x)]$
4. $[\sim(\exists x)(\varphi_x \cdot \sim \psi_x)] \equiv [(x)(\varphi_x \supset \psi_x)]$

An instance of the first of these four logical equivalences has been proved by Examples 106 and 107. Let us now prove the remaining three logical equivalences. We must prove, for each of these, that each member of the biconditional can be deduced from the other. This we shall do, for each equivalence, by constructing two proofs, one for each implication involved. The proof of the second logical equivalence follows:

Case α

$\diagup \therefore \sim(x)(\varphi_x \supset \psi_x)$

1. $(\exists x)(\varphi_x \cdot \sim \psi_x)$ Pr.
2. $\sim(x)\sim(\varphi_x \cdot \sim \psi_x)$ 1, D_V
3. $\therefore \sim(x)(\varphi_x \supset \psi_x)$ 2, $S(D_{II})$

Case β

$\diagup \therefore (\exists x)(\varphi_x \cdot \sim \psi_x)$

1. $\sim(x)(\varphi_x \supset \psi_x)$ Pr.
2. $\sim(x)\sim(\varphi_x \cdot \sim \psi_x)$ 1, $S(D_{II})$
3. $\therefore (\exists x)(\varphi_x \cdot \sim \psi_x)$ 2, D_V

The proof of the third logical equivalence is:

Case α

$\diagup \therefore (x)(\varphi_x \supset \sim \psi_x)$

1. $\sim(\exists x)(\varphi_x \cdot \psi_x)$ Pr.
2. $\sim \sim(x)\sim(\varphi_x \cdot \psi_x)$ 1, $S(D_V)$

3. $(x)\sim(\varphi_x \cdot \psi_x)$ 2, A_{11}

4. $(x)\sim(\varphi_x \cdot \sim \sim\psi_x)$ 3, S(DN)

5. $\therefore (x)(\varphi_x \supset \sim\psi_x)$ 4, S(D_{II})

Case β

$$/ \therefore \sim(\exists x)(\varphi_x \cdot \psi_x)$$

1. $(x)(\varphi_x \supset \sim\psi_x)$ Pr.

2. $\sim \sim(x)(\varphi_x \supset \sim\psi_x)$ 1, A_{10}

3. $\sim \sim(x) \sim(\varphi_x \cdot \sim \sim\psi_x)$ 2, S(D_{II})

4. $\sim(\exists x)(\varphi_x \cdot \sim \sim\psi_x)$ 3, S(D_V)

5. $\therefore \sim(\exists x)(\varphi_x \cdot \psi_x)$ 4, S(DN)

And finally, the proof of the fourth logical equivalence is:

Case α

$$/ \therefore (x)(\varphi_x \supset \psi_x)$$

1. $\sim(\exists x)(\varphi_x \cdot \sim\psi_x)$ Pr.

2. $\sim \sim(x)\sim(\varphi_x \cdot \sim\psi_x)$ 1, S(D_V)

3. $(x)\sim(\varphi_x \cdot \sim\psi_x)$ 2, A_{11}

4. $\therefore (x)(\varphi_x \supset \psi_x)$ 3, S(D_{II})

Case β

$$/ \therefore \sim(\exists x)(\varphi_x \cdot \sim\psi_x)$$

1. $(x)(\varphi_x \supset \psi_x)$ Pr.

3. $(x)\sim(\varphi_x \cdot \sim\psi_x)$ 1, S(D_{II})

3. $\sim \sim(x)\sim(\varphi_x \cdot \sim\psi_x)$ 2, A_{10}

4. $\therefore \sim(\exists x)(\varphi_x \cdot \sim\psi_x)$ 3, S(D_V)

We have previously given three rules for the transformation of existentially quantified statements to universally quantified statements, and vice versa. These three rules, as we noted, apply when the statements are of the general form $(\exists\alpha)S$ or of the general form $(\alpha)S$. A look at the four logical equivalences we have just established, however, reveals some specialized rules which obtain when S is of the form $\varphi_x \supset \psi_x$ (if the statement is a *universally* quantified one), or of the form $\varphi_x \cdot \psi_x$ (if the statement is an *existentially* quantified one). These rules follow:

1. Change the sign before the quantifier. (I.e., if there is a tilde, remove it; if not, add one.)
2. Change the quantifier. (I.e., if it is of the form $(\exists\alpha)$, change it to one of the form (α), and vice versa.)
3. Change the main operator of the statement within parentheses. (If the operator is $\cdot$, in an *existentially* quantified statement, it becomes $\supset$ in a *universally* quantified statement; and vice versa.)

4. Change the sign of the instance of ψ_x. (I.e., if there is a tilde before it, remove it; if not, add one.)

Now that we have familiarized ourselves with the transformations from one type of quantification to another, let us briefly turn our attention to a consideration of negative quantified statements, i.e., statements of the forms $\sim(\exists\alpha)S$ and $\sim(\alpha)S$. As we have mentioned earlier, the tilde, in these forms, indicates the negation of the entire expression, $(\exists\alpha)S$ or $(\alpha)S$, and does not indicate the negation of the quantifier. Statements can be positive or negative, logical operators cannot; and since $(\exists\alpha)$ and (α) represent logical operators, it does not make sense to speak of them as negated. One might indicate that, in statements of the forms $\sim(\exists\alpha)S$ and $\sim(\alpha)S$, the entire expression is negated by the tilde, by writing them thus: $\sim[(\exists\alpha)S]$ and $\sim[(\alpha)S]$. We adopt the convention of omitting the square brackets.

A realization that $\sim(\exists\alpha)S$ and $\sim(\alpha)S$ are negative statement forms suggests something about the employment of statements exhibiting these forms in arguments involving quantification. Suppose, for example, we are given an argument involving the negative statement, "There aren't any people living today who fought in the Battle of Bunker Hill", which we shall symbolize as $\sim(\exists x)[(P_x \cdot L_x) \cdot F_x]$. We cannot instantiate this statement, in a proof of validity, by the use of A_{15}, even supposing the restriction on A_{15} would not be violated. For in that case we should get $(P_x{}^* \cdot L_x{}^*) \cdot F_x{}^*$, i.e., "an individual is living who fought at the Battle of Bunker Hill", when we had previously denied that any such individual could be alive today. The reason why A_{15} cannot here be used should be rather obvious: A_{15} involves two *positive* statements; and $\sim(\exists x)[(P_x \cdot L_x) \cdot F_x]$, being negative, cannot be treated as an instance of one of them, as an attempted diagram will reveal. We shall therefore have to transform our statement, $\sim(\exists x)[(P_x \cdot L_x) \cdot F_x]$, into its *positive* equivalent as a *universally* quantified statement, namely, $(x)[(P_x \cdot L_x) \supset \sim F_x]$, and instantiate by means of A_{13}. We may therefore formulate the rule that, when using A_{13} or A_{15}, *one must always instantiate from a positive statement.*

This problem does not arise with regard to A_{14} and A_{16}, for *any* negative statement, when generalized, results in a *positive* statement. Thus, a statement of the form $\sim\Phi_\alpha{}^*$ might be generalized to a statement of the form $(\alpha)\sim\Phi_\alpha$, or to a statement of the form $(\exists\alpha)\sim\Phi_\alpha$, both of which are *positive*.

Before we apply what we have learned in this section to the construction of proofs of validity, let us introduce a notational convention. When we use any of the logical equivalences involving quantification which we discussed in this section, in constructing a proof of validity; let us write, in the "reasons" column of our proof, "Q", meaning "equivalence of quantification". Thus, if $\sim(x)(\varphi_x \supset \psi_x)$ is the first statement in a proof, we can go directly to $(\exists x)(\varphi_x \cdot \sim\psi_x)$, giving as our reason, "1, Q".

EXERCISES

GROUP A

566. For those statements in the set of exercises (481–505) which you previously translated by the use of the *universal* quantifier, give the equivalents of these statements, using the *existential* quantifier. Proofs of the equivalences are *not* required in this exercise (or in exercise 567).

567. For those statements in the set of exercises (536–550) which you previously translated by the use of the *existential* quantifier, give the equivalents of these statements, using the *universal* quantifier.

GROUP B

For each of the following statements, (a) translate it into symbolic form. If the statement in English is given as a *universally* quantified statement, translate it by the use of the *universal* quantifier. If the statement in English is given as an *existentially* quantified statement, translate it by the use of the *existential* quantifier. Then, (b) give the equivalent of the statement using the other quantifier. Proofs of the equivalences are *not* required. Use the suggested predicate notation.

568. Some cats have fur.   (C, F)
569. No cat doesn't have fur.   (C, F)
570. It is not the case that some cats don't have fur.   (C, F)
571. All Cheshire cats smile.   (C, S)
572. Not all Cheshire cats don't smile.   (C, S)
573. There aren't any monkeys that don't have tails.   (M, T)
574. All monkeys don't have tails.   (M, T)
575. It is not the case that some monkeys don't have tails.   (M, T)
576. There aren't some monkeys that don't have tails.   (M, T)
577. It is not the case that there aren't some monkeys that don't have tails. (M, T)
578. Not all monkeys have tails.   (M, T)
579. It is not the case that all monkeys don't have tails.   (M, T)
580. It is not the case that not all monkeys do not have tails.   (M, T)

GROUP C

Construct a proof of validity for each of the following arguments, using the suggested predicate notation:

581. There aren't some humans who aren't mortal; and there aren't some mortals who aren't rational animals. Hence there aren't some humans who are not rational animals. (H, M, R)

582. There aren't some humans who aren't featherless bipeds. All featherless bipeds are rational animals. Therefore there aren't some humans who aren't rational animals. (H, B, R)

583. There aren't some humans who aren't mortal, although there are some humans who aren't students. Hence some mortals aren't students. (H, M, S)

584. Not all arguments are valid. There aren't any arguments which are both sound and not valid. Hence not all arguments are sound. (A, V, S)

585. Not all concerts are enjoyable. There aren't any concerts which aren't time-consuming. Hence not all time-consuming things are enjoyable. (C, E, T)

586. No scientists are narrow-minded. Some bigots are narrow-minded. Therefore not all bigots are scientists. (S, N, B)

587. No student who is not conscientious gets good grades. Not all students don't get good grades. Hence not all students are not conscientious. (S, C, G)

588. There aren't some birds that don't have feathers. All things which have feathers have wings. Not all birds don't build nests. Hence not all things with wings don't build nests. (B, F, W, N)

589. There aren't some birds which don't have feathers, and there aren't some feathered things which don't hatch from eggs. All crows are birds. Hence there aren't any crows which don't hatch from eggs. (B, F, H, C)

590. Every raw egg-white contains avidin. Everything which contains avidin inhibits the action of biotin in the human body. There aren't any things which inhibit the action of biotin in the human body that can't cause premature aging in humans. Hence every raw egg-white can cause premature aging in humans. (E, A, B, P)

§38. The Application of Truth Tables to Arguments Involving Quantification

Perhaps the question has occurred to the reader, "Can one prove validity and invalidity, consistency and inconsistency, of arguments involving quantification, by means of truth tables, just as one does for arguments which do not involve quantification?" The answer to this query is *"Yes."* However, one cannot assign truth values to the quantified statements as they stand. Consider the following argument:

EXAMPLE 108

Some birds fly. Some mammals fly. Therefore some birds are mammals.
(B, F, M)

Symbolically, this argument is translated as follows:

EXAMPLE 109

$(\exists x)(B_x \cdot F_x)$
$(\exists x)(M_x \cdot F_x)$
$\therefore (\exists x)(B_x \cdot M_x)$

If, in assigning truth values to the variables, we assign a certain value to F_x in the first premise, we would have to assign the same value to it in the second premise (using the *reductio ad absurdum* method). But we know that the restriction on A_{15} would make the instantiation of these two premises contain not the same F_x, but rather two *different* variables, say F_x^* and F_x^{**} (using the single and double asterisks to indicate the two different instantiations required by the restriction on A_{15}). Accordingly, to assign truth values to the quantified premises themselves will not allow for such differences of instantiation. There is, however, no reason why F_x^* and F_x^{**} should necessarily have the same truth value, since they are not identical, but different.

We shall, then, have to assign truth values not to the variables in the quantified argument itself, but rather to those in a hypothetical conditional statement corresponding to a legitimate instantiation of it. If the premises are instantiated thus: $B_x^* \cdot F_x^*$ and $M_x^{**} \cdot F_x^{**}$, then the only meaning that an instantiation of the conclusion can have will be in terms of an inclusive disjunction, i.e., the conclusion will hold for either or both individuals specified in the two instantiations, thus:

$$(B_x^* \cdot M_x^*) \vee (B_x^{**} \cdot M_x^{**})$$

The hypothetical conditional statement corresponding to the instance of the argument which we shall test is:

$$[(B_x^* \cdot F_x^*) \cdot (M_x^{**} \cdot F_x^{**})] \supset [(B_x^* \cdot M_x^*) \vee (B_x^{**} \cdot M_x^{**})]$$

A truth table may be constructed for this hypothetical conditional statement, but it would be quite long. Let us therefore apply the *reductio ad absurdum* method of testing validity and invalidity. We find that the argument is invalid, because there is a possible case in which the hypothetical conditional statement corresponding to the instantiation of the argument may be false, thus:

$$[(B_x^* \cdot F_x) \cdot (M_x^{**} \cdot F_x^{**})] \supset [(B_x^* \cdot M_x^*) \vee (B_x^{**} \cdot M_x^{**})]$$

T T T T T T T   F   T F F F F F T

If we encounter an argument with two or more existentially quantified premises and one or more universally quantified premises, each universally quantified premise will have to be instantiated as many different times as there are existentially quantified premises. Let us consider the following premise set:

EXAMPLE 110

All humans are mortal. Some humans are long-lived. Some mortals are quadrupeds.   (H, M, L, Q)

The two existentially quantified premises, as usual, will be instantiated first:

$$H_x^* \cdot L_x^*$$
$$M_x^{**} \cdot Q_x^{**}$$

Now, since a universally quantified statement may be instantiated with regard to *any* individual, and since two individuals have already been specified in our existential instantiations (namely x* and x**), we shall instantiate our universally quantified premise twice to insure that it covers both individuals, thus:

$$H_x^* \supset M_x^*$$
$$H_x^{**} \supset M_x^{**}$$

These are both legitimate instantiations of our universally quantified premise. The conjunction of the required instantiations of the premises, then, will be:

$$[(H_x{}^* \cdot L_x{}^*) \cdot (M_x{}^{**} \cdot Q_x{}^{**})\ ] \cdot [(H_x{}^* \supset M_x{}^*\ ) \cdot (H_x{}^{**} \supset M_x{}^{**})]$$

If the conclusion of the argument were universally quantified, say, "Therefore, all quadrupeds are long-lived", we should have to test a double instance of the argument, this time by stating the conclusion in the form of a conjunction, since a universal statement would be true, if at all, of *both* individuals specified:

$$\therefore\ (Q_x{}^* \supset L_x{}^*) \cdot (Q_x{}^{**} \supset L_x{}^{**})$$

The *reductio ad absurdum* method proves this argument invalid as follows:

$$\{\ [(H_x{}^* \cdot L_x{}^*) \cdot (M_x{}^{**} \cdot Q_x{}^{**})] \cdot [(H_x{}^* \supset M_x{}^*) \cdot (H_x{}^{**} \supset M_x{}^{**})]\}$$

T T T T T T T T T T T T T

$$\supset [(Q_x{}^* \supset L_x{}^*) \cdot (Q_x{}^{**} \supset L_x{}^{**})]$$

F   T T T F T   F F

When instantiations are made as specified in this section, the familiar consistency and inconsistency tests, as well as the validity and invalidity tests, can be performed for any argument involving quantification.

EXERCISES

Decide, by the *reductio ad absurdum* method, whether each argument is consistent or inconsistent. If consistent, test further for validity by the *reductio ad absurdum* method. For those arguments which the *reductio ad absurdum* tests reveal to be both consistent and valid, construct a formal proof of validity. Use the suggested notation.

591. All grass is verdant. Not all grass isn't edible, although there isn't any grass which is edible. Hence not all edible things aren't verdant. (G, V, E)

592. All goldfish swim. No goldfish fly. Therefore nothing that swims flies. (G, S, F)

593. All ghosts haunt. Some ghosts scare people. Hence some things that scare people haunt. (G, H, S)

594. All goldfish swim. Cleo is a goldfish and/or Cleo swims; but Cleo doesn't swim. Hence Cleo isn't a goldfish. (G, S; $_x$, $_c$)

595. Some goldfish are small. Some small things are rodents. Therefore some goldfish are rodents. (G, S, R)

596. Some animals swim. All dogs are animals. Therefore some dogs swim. (A, S, D)

597. All cats purr. All cats have fur, but all things with fur don't purr. Thus some things with fur don't purr. (C, P, F)

598. Some cats purr. All things which purr are friendly. Tabby is a cat who is not friendly. Hence Tabby doesn't purr. (C, P, F; ₓ, ₜ)

599. There aren't any dinosaurs with purple tails, although some birds have purple tails. Some dinosaurs aren't birds. Hence not all birds have purple tails. (D, P, B)

600. All Platonists believe in a transcendental realm of Ideas. All Aristotelians believe in immanent Forms. Everyone who is not a Platonist is an Aristotelian. Hence everyone who doesn't believe in a transcendental realm of Ideas believes in immanent Forms. (P, I, A, F)

601. Some insects are poisonous, and some poisonous things are lethal. All lethal things should be avoided. Therefore all insects should be avoided. (I, P, L, A)

602. Some apples are green, and some green things are poisonous. All apples are delicious. Therefore some delicious things are poisonous. (A, G, P, D)

603. All Pythagoreans believe that number is the essence of the universe. All those who believe that number is the essence of the universe believe that ultimate principles of the universe can be conceived geometrically. Einstein was a Pythagorean and/or he believed that the ultimate principles of the universe can be conceived geometrically. Einstein did not believe that the ultimate principles of the universe can be conceived geometrically. Hence Einstein was not a Pythagorean, although he believed that number is the essence of the universe. (P, N, G; ₓ, ₑ)

604. Some coins are collectors' items. Not all coins aren't quite ordinary. There aren't any coins that aren't money. No money isn't negotiable. Therefore all things which are collectors' items are negotiable, and some things which are quite ordinary are collectors' items. (C, I, O, M, N)

605. All dogs are carnivorous. Some carnivorous things are vicious. Some vicious things bite. Some things that bite are not intelligent. Therefore no dog is intelligent. (D, C, V, B, I)

§39. Proving Quantified Arguments Valid by the Conditional and Indirect Methods

The conditional and indirect methods can be used in proving the validity of arguments involving quantified statements, if a slight modification is made in their application. Previously, when using these methods, we made an assumption based on the *conclusion* of the original argument. Thus, the conditional method would be used by assuming the antecedent of the conclusion when the conclusion was a hypothetical conditional statement. Or, when the indirect method was used, we would assume the negation of the conclusion. This we can still do in arguments with one or more quantified premises, provided their conclusions are not quantified. However, when we consider arguments whose conclusions are quantified, we shall not make a *quantified* assumption, but rather an assumption based on an instantiation of the conclusion. Let us consider an example. Suppose we wish to prove the validity of the following argument:

EXAMPLE 111

All philanthropists who are kind are generous and unselfish. All who contribute to worthy endeavors are philanthropists. Hence all who are kind are not contributors to worthy endeavors if they are not unselfish. (P, K, G, U, C)

A proof of the validity of this argument, using both the conditional and indirect methods, follows:

EXAMPLE 112

$$/ \therefore (x)[K_x \supset (\sim U_x \supset \sim C_x)]$$

1. $(x)[(P_x \cdot K_x) \supset (G_x \cdot U_x)]$	Pr.	
2. $(x)(C_x \supset P_x)$	Pr.	
3. $(P_x^* \cdot K_x^*) \supset (G_x^* \cdot U_x^*)$	1, A_{13}	
4. $C_x^* \supset P_x^*$	2, A_{13}	
5. K_x^*	Assump $/ \therefore \sim U_x^* \supset \sim C_x^*$	
6. $\sim U_x^*$	Assump $/ \therefore \sim C_x^*$	
7. $\sim \sim C_x^*$	Assump (IP)	
8. C_x^*	7, A_{11}	
9. P_x^*	4, 8, A_1	
10. $P_x^* \cdot K_x^*$	9, 5, A_9	
11. $G_x^* \cdot U_x^*$	3, 10, A_1	
12. U_x^*	11, A_8; A_7	
13. $U_x^* \vee \sim C_x^*$	12, A_{12}	
14. $\sim C_x^*$	13, 6, A_4	
15. $\sim U_x^* \supset \sim C_x^*$	6–14, CP	
16. $K_x^* \supset (\sim U_x^* \supset \sim C_x^*)$	5–15, CP	
17. $\therefore (x)[K_x \supset (\sim U_x \supset \sim C_x)]$	16, A_{14}	

In this proof of validity, we first instantiated the premises (in statements 3 and 4), because we cannot, of course, proceed further without doing this first even in a *formal* proof of validity. Then, we assumed the antecedent of the instantiation of the conclusion, namely K_x^*, in statement 5; and indicated in our proof (in the right-hand column) that from this assumption, plus the original premises, we would conclude the consequent of the instantiation of the conclusion, namely $\sim U_x^* \supset \sim C_x^*$. This we accordingly do, in statement 15; whereby statement 16, which says that the assumption implies $\sim U_x^* \supset \sim C_x^*$, is justified. Then, from statement 16, we generalize to the desired conclusion of the original argument, in statement 17, by A_{14}.

Within the scope of the assumption, K_x^*, in statement 5, however; two more assumptions are also made. Since, from the assumption of statement 5, and the original premises, what we are to conclude, namely $\sim U_x^* \supset \sim C_x^*$, is itself a hypothetical conditional statement, we may again make another assumption, namely the antecedent of this hypothetical conditional statement, $\sim U_x^*$, from which we shall conclude $\sim C_x^*$, its consequent, as statement 6 indicates. And again, in statement 7, we apply the method of indirect proof and assume the negation of $\sim C_x^*$. The scope of the third assumption ends at statement 13, as the appropriate indentations in the proof indicate.

Had the conclusion of this argument been stated as a negative existential statement, such as $\sim (\exists x)[(K_x \cdot \sim U_x) \cdot C_x]$, instead of its positive universal equivalent, we would, when using the conditional and indirect methods (either separately or together), make an assumption based on the positive universal equivalent of the conclusion. Likewise, for an argument whose conclusion is a negative universal statement, we would make an assumption based on an instantiation of the positive existential equivalent of the conclusion.

Let us compare the rather easy proof of validity in Example 112, for the argument of Example 111, with the formal proof in Example 113 for the validity of the same argument. Note that since the abbreviated method has been used in the proof in Example 113, there are even more operations involved than the twenty-one steps would suggest.

EXAMPLE 113

$$/ \therefore (x)[K_x \supset (\sim U_x \supset \sim C_x)]$$

1. $(x)[(P_x \cdot K_x) \supset (G_x \cdot U_x)]$	Pr.
2. $(x)(C_x \supset P_x)$	Pr.
3. $(P_x^* \cdot K_x^*) \supset (G_x^* \cdot U_x^*)$	1, A_{13}
4. $C_x^* \supset P_x^*$	2, A_{13}
5. $P_x^* \supset [K_x^* \supset (G_x^* \cdot U_x^*)]$	3, Exp
6. $C_x^* \supset [K_x^* \supset (G_x^* \cdot U_x^*)]$	4, 5, A_3
7. $(C_x^* \cdot K_x^*) \supset (G_x^* \cdot U_x^*)$	6, Exp
8. $\sim[\sim \sim(C_x^* \cdot K_x^*)$ $\cdot \sim(G_x^* \cdot U_x^*)]$	7, D_{II}; S(DN)
9. $\sim(C_x^* \cdot K_x^*) \vee (G_x^* \cdot U_x^*)$	8, D_I
10. $\sim(\sim \sim C_x^* \cdot K_x^*) \vee (G_x^* \cdot U_x^*)$	9, S(DN)
11. $\sim(\sim \sim C_x^* \cdot \sim \sim K_x^*)$ $\vee (G_x^* \cdot U_x^*)$	10, S(DN)
12. $(\sim C_x^* \vee \sim K_x^*) \vee (G_x^* \cdot U_x^*)$	11, S(D_I)
13. $[(\sim C_x^* \vee \sim K_x^*) \vee G_x^*]$ $\cdot [(\sim C_x^* \vee \sim K_x^*) \vee U_x^*]$	12, Dist
14. $(\sim C_x^* \vee \sim K_x^*) \vee U_x^*$	13, A_8; A_7
15. $(\sim K_x^* \vee \sim C_x^*) \vee U_x^*$	14, S(Com)
16. $\sim K_x^* \vee (\sim C_x^* \vee U_x^*)$	15, LE$\{[(P \vee Q) \vee R]$ $\equiv [P \vee (Q \vee R)]\}$
17. $\sim K_x^* \vee (U_x^* \vee \sim C_x^*)$	16, S(Com)
18. $\sim \sim K_x^* \supset (U_x^* \vee \sim C_x^*)$	17, D_I; D_{II}
19. $K_x^* \supset (U_x^* \vee \sim C_x^*)$	18, S(DN)
20. $K_x^* \supset (\sim U_x^* \supset \sim C_x^*)$	19, S(D_I); S(D_{II})
21. $\therefore (x)[K_x \supset (\sim U_x \supset \sim C_x)]$	20, A_{14}

EXERCISES

GROUP A

606. Explain how the methods of conditional proof and indirect proof may be applied to arguments involving quantified statements.

607. You have already constructed formal proofs for the validity of the arguments of exercises 581 to 590. Now construct proofs of validity for them in which you use either the conditional method, or the indirect method, or a combination of both.

GROUP B

For each of the following arguments, construct a proof of validity using either the conditional method, or the indirect method, or a combination of both.

608. All flying saucers which are visible are space ships and extremely rapid. There aren't any interplanetary vessels which aren't flying saucers. Hence there aren't any non-rapid things which are both interplanetary vessels and visible. (F, V, S, R, I)

609. Some birds have wings and/or feet. Everything with feet perambulates, and everything with wings is airborne. Accordingly some birds perambulate and/or are airborne. (B, W, F, P, A)

610. Everything which is a space ship only if it is airborne, is friendly and/or hostile. Friendly things should be welcomed, whereas hostile things should be discouraged. So everything which is a space ship only if it is airborne should be discouraged and/or welcomed. (S, A, F, H, W, D)

CHAPTER SIX

Conclusion

§40. Final Remarks

Symbolic logic is regarded by many philosophers today as the most significant branch of philosophy. One contemporary philosopher, A. J. Ayer, has even gone so far as to proclaim that philosophy itself is but a branch of logic. Whether one wishes to go this far or not is a matter of one's personal philosophy. At any rate, a realization of the important function of logic is evident to contemporary philosophers. If one analyzes clearly the logical problems involved in many of the topics with which philosophy concerns itself, the solutions are easier to find. Sometimes the problems of philosophy are seen, on logical analysis, not to be problems at all, but merely pseudo-problems, arising from the misuse of language. Thus, for example, when logic introduces two symbols, V and Ⓥ, to distinguish the two meanings of the English word "or", many misunderstandings based on the confusion of these two senses of the word can be avoided.

Logic is indispensable to the philosopher today, but it is not a panacea whereby all the problems of philosophy can be solved. It is a tool, an *ancillary propadeutic,* as it has been called. But it is an extremely useful, and frequently an indispensable, tool. It is a tool not only for philosophy, but for all aspects of life.

We have, in this book, encountered some awkward English expressions which this tool has helped us untangle—expressions beginning, for example, with "The following is not the case, namely that either • • •". If it be argued that such examples are unrealistic, because people never really talk that way, let it be replied that if one can unravel such expressions, he will have little trouble with those he actually does encounter frequently. What *is* realistic is recognizing the need for developing the tool of logic. The musician does not regard as unrealistic his arduous practice of scales, even though he never plans to give a recital consisting of the 24 major and minor scales. He is developing the tool of his profession. So the student of logic develops the tool of his profession, whatever it be; and especially of that extremely important profession in which we are all engaged, *life*.

In this book we have presented an elementary system of symbolic logic, which, it is hoped, the reader will find useful no matter in what pursuit he is engaged. The housewife who tries to budget her time to get her house work done in a certain time is using logic. "If I wash the dishes now, I'll have time to bake that cake I promised Arthur. I'll wash the dishes now. Thus I'll have time to bake the cake." Or, to bring the example out of the commonplace, the research scientist will need logic to check various calculations and predictions.

Decisions for action are based on knowledge of consequences. "If such-and-such, then thus-and-so." Often the outcomes are of monumental significance to us and to society as a whole. If we have not examined the implications of premises, or the validity of arguments, we may not, in vitally important situations, be prepared to reject or accept a future course of action, and to decide whether or not we wish to live by conclusions which follow from a given set of premises.

Human situations frequently involve the use of induction, as well as of deduction. The systematization of thought required by the study of deductive logic is nevertheless invaluable. The person who knows no more logic than is contained in this volume can benefit immeasurably. Yet he has by no means learned all there is to know about logic. Much more is to be learned about symbolic logic; and induction has hardly been touched upon.

Depending on one's special needs, one may or may not wish to acquire a further knowledge of logic. There are some good books in advanced symbolic logic, as well as excellent ones in induction, which the reader can profitably pursue. John Stuart Mill's *A System of Logic* is still excellent for the study of induction; and Aristotle's *Organon* can be studied by those interested in the historical beginnings of deduction. Whitehead and Russell's *Principia Mathematica* is the major work in symbolic logic today, but it is an extremely difficult one. Easier would be some advanced college textbook in symbolic logic, such as Irving M. Copi's *Symbolic Logic,* or J. B. Rosser's *Logic for Mathematicians.*

Yet it is hoped that, even if the reader never looks between the covers of any other logic book than this one, he will still have gained some measure of benefit.

§41. Summary of Logical Principles

Valid Argument Forms:

A_1 (*modus ponens*)
   $P \supset Q$
   P
   $\therefore Q$

A_2 (*modus tollens*)
   $P \supset Q$
   $\sim Q$
   $\therefore \sim P$

A_3 (hypothetical syllogism)
   $P \supset Q$
   $Q \supset R$
   $\therefore P \supset R$

A_4 (disjunctive syllogism)
   $P \lor Q$
   $\sim P$
   $\therefore Q$

A_5 (commutativity of inclusive disjunction)
   $P \lor Q$
   $\therefore Q \lor P$

A_6 (constructive dilemma)
   $P \supset Q$
   $R \supset S$
   $P \lor R$
   $\therefore Q \lor S$

A_7 (simplification)
   $P \cdot Q$
   $\therefore P$

A_8 (commutativity of conjunction)
   $P \cdot Q$
   $\therefore Q \cdot P$

A_9 (conjunction)
   P
   Q
   $\therefore P \cdot Q$

A_{10} (double negation)
   P
   $\therefore \sim \sim P$

A_{11} (double negation)
   $\sim \sim P$
   $\therefore P$

A_{12} (addition)
   P
   $\therefore P \lor Q$

A_{13} (universal instantiation)
   $(\alpha)\Phi\alpha$
   $\therefore \Phi\alpha^*$

A_{14} (universal generalization)
   $\Phi\alpha^*$
   $\therefore (\alpha)\Phi\alpha$

A_{15} (existential instantiation)
   $(\exists\alpha)\Phi\alpha$
   $\therefore \Phi\alpha^*$

   [*Restriction:* α^* designates an individual which has not been previously mentioned in the proof of validity.]

A_{16} (existential generalization)
   $\Phi\alpha^*$
   $\therefore (\exists\alpha)\Phi\alpha$

Definitions:
D_I: $P \lor Q =_{df} \sim(\sim P \cdot \sim Q)$
D_{II}: $P \supset Q =_{df} \sim(P \cdot \sim Q)$
D_{III}: $P \equiv Q =_{df} \sim(P \cdot \sim Q) \cdot \sim(Q \cdot \sim P)$
D_{IV}: $P \, \circled{v} \, Q =_{df} \sim(\sim P \cdot \sim Q) \cdot \sim(P \cdot Q)$
D_V: $(\exists \alpha)S =_{df} \sim(\alpha)\sim S$

Logical Equivalences:
Trans: $(P \supset Q) \equiv (\sim Q \supset \sim P)$
Exp: $[(P \cdot Q) \supset R] \equiv [P \supset (Q \supset R)]$
Com: $(P \, \circled{v} \, Q) \equiv (Q \, \circled{v} \, P)$
       $(P \equiv Q) \equiv (Q \equiv P)$
B/D: (Case α) $(P \equiv Q) \equiv \sim(P \, \circled{v} \, Q)$
                  $\sim(P \equiv Q) \equiv (P \, \circled{v} \, Q)$
       (Case β) $(P \equiv Q) \equiv (\sim P \, \circled{v} \, Q)$
                  $(P \equiv Q) \equiv (P \, \circled{v} \, \sim Q)$
                  $(\sim P \equiv Q) \equiv (P \, \circled{v} \, Q)$
                  $(P \equiv \sim Q) \equiv (P \, \circled{v} \, Q)$
Dist: $[P \cdot (Q \lor R)] \equiv [(P \cdot Q) \lor (P \cdot R)]$
       $[P \lor (Q \cdot R)] \equiv [(P \lor Q) \cdot (P \lor R)]$

Equivalences used only with the Principle of Substitution:
       S(DN): $P \equiv \sim \sim P$
       S(Com): $(P \cdot Q) \equiv (Q \cdot P)$
               $(P \lor Q) \equiv (Q \lor P)$

Aristotelian Logic

The first major work in the science of deductive logic is the ancient *Organon* of Aristotle. Not only is this the first, but it is the *sole* work of major importance in the field until quite recently. In the nineteenth century, the works of Schröder and Frege, among others, appeared; and early in the twentieth century the monumental *Principia Mathematica* of Whitehead and Russell appeared. The present textbook has presented, in elementary form, the basic points of a system comparable to that of the *Principia Mathematica*.

The logic we have studied is not really a "new" logic, for there are many elements of our modern logic which were realized by Aristotle. What is new is the scope of the logic (Aristotle is incomplete) and the symbolic notation which we have explained in this book.

A look at Aristotelian logic, however cursory, will be enlightening. It will give us some indication of the history of our science, and make for a fuller appreciation of those intellects, ancient and modern, who have furthered the science of deductive logic.

Sometimes Aristotelian logic is referred to as "classical logic", which is perhaps a bit more accurate than the appellation "Aristotelian logic". For this body of logic, while basically that of Aristotle, has undergone various revisions, especially in the means of presentation, throughout the ages. Thus Aristotle and tradition combine to give us deductive logic as it was known prior to the advent of modern symbolic logic.

Let us take a brief, and admittedly incomplete, look at Aristotelian or classical logic. We shall use our knowledge of symbolic logic to help us understand this older system.

Aristotelian logic classifies statements having two terms (like "cat" and "black" in "All cats are black") into four kinds:

First, the *universal affirmative* statement, like "All cats are black."

This is of the form "All A's are B", or, in modern symbolic notation, $(x)(\varphi_x \supset \psi_x)$.

Second, there is the *existential affirmative* statement (also sometimes known as "the particular affirmative statement"), like "Some cats are black." This is of the form "Some A's are B", or, in symbolic notation, $(\exists x)(\varphi_x \cdot \psi_x)$.

Third, there is the *universal negative* statement, such as "No cats are black." This is of the form "No A's are B", or, symbolically, $(x)(\varphi_x \supset \sim \psi_x)$.

And finally, there is the *existential negative* statement (also sometimes called "the particular negative statement"), such as "Some cats are not black." This is of the form "Some A's are not B", or, in symbolic notation, $(\exists x)(\varphi_x \cdot \sim \psi_x)$.

These four kinds of statements are called, respectively, "A", "I", "E", and "O" statements. The traditional reason for this designation is that "A" and "I", for the two *affirmative* kinds of statements, are the first two vowels of the Latin word, *affirmo,* meaning "I affirm"; and that "E" and "O", for the two *negative* kinds of statements, are the two vowels of the Latin word, *nego,* meaning "I deny". (One would suspect that tradition has somewhat assisted Aristotle with his Latin, since his tongue was Greek.)

The A, I, E, and O statements are traditionally arranged as follows, in what is known as "The Square of Opposition":

THE ARISTOTELIAN SQUARE OF OPPOSITION

A	E
Universal Affirmative	*Universal Negative*
All A's are B	No A's are B
$(x)(\varphi_x \supset \psi_x)$	$(x)(\varphi_x \supset \sim\psi_x)$
I	O
Existential Affirmative	*Existential Negative*
Some A's are B	Some A's are not B
$(\exists x)(\varphi_x \cdot \psi_x)$	$(\exists x)(\varphi_x \cdot \sim\psi_x)$

Various types of what is known as "immediate inference" (and not, as one student called it, "immediate ignorance") obtain among these four kinds of statements. By "immediate inference" is meant an argument with *one* premise only, and a conclusion derived directly from it without the need of any auxiliary statements. An example, in the familiar notation, follows:

EXAMPLE OF IMMEDIATE INFERENCE

$(x) (\varphi_x \supset \psi_x)$
$\therefore \sim (\exists x)(\varphi_x \cdot \sim \psi_x)$

"Mediate inference" is the name given to arguments with more than one premise, such as the following:

EXAMPLE OF MEDIATE INFERENCE

$(x)(\varphi_x \supset \psi_x)$
$(x)(\psi_x \supset \chi_x)$
$\therefore (x)(\varphi_x \supset \chi_x)$

The relations which obtain among the four kinds of statements of Aristotelian logic, and which indicate types of immediate inference, are shown below:

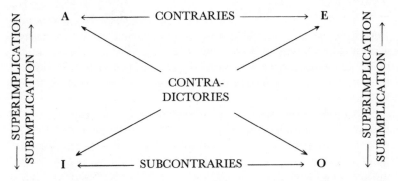

Let us now show, in terms of symbolic logic, what these various types of immediate inference are:

1. *Contradictoriness.* A and O statements contradict one another, as do E and I statements. By this is meant that if the one is true, the other is false, and vice versa. This is our old friend, the exclusive disjunction. Accordingly, in terms of symbolic logic, we may indicate what this relation of contradictoriness is, as follows:

$$A \text{ ⓥ } O$$
$$E \text{ ⓥ } I$$

2. *Contrariety*. Contrariety is a relation which holds between the A and E statements. Two contrary statements can not both be true, although both can be false. Using c for a moment (to stand for "is contrary to"), let us construct a truth table for A c E. It is:

A	c	E
T	F	T
T	T	F
F	T	T
F	T	F

This is the negation of $A \cdot E$. Thus, the relation of contrariety may be defined as $\sim(A \cdot E)$.

3. *Subcontrariety*. This relation holds between I and O statements, and is our old friend, the inclusive disjunction: at least one of the two statements standing in the relation of subcontrariety must be true. Thus, $I \lor O$.

4. *Superimplication*. If the A statement is true, then the corresponding I statement is true; but if the A statement is false, then the corresponding I statement may be either true or false. This is what is meant by our horseshoe, so we may express this relationship as $A \supset I$. Further, the same relation obtains between E and O statements, thus: $E \supset O$.

5. *Subimplication*. Let us introduce, temporarily, the sign $\supset_s$, meaning "subimplies", and see how we can define $I \supset_s A$ and $O \supset_s E$. What is meant by subimplication is that, in these statements, if the first member is true, the second may be true or false; but if the first is false, the second must also be false. The truth table, accordingly, looks like this:

I	$\supset_s$	A
(or: O	$\supset_s$	E)
T	T	T
T	T	F
F	F	T
F	T	F

This happens to be the truth table for $\sim(\sim I \cdot A)$ (as well as for $\sim(\sim O \cdot E)$), which, accordingly, is the meaning of subimplication in terms of symbolic logic.

Note that each of these five relationships of Aristotelian immediate inference is definable in terms of our functionally complete set of operators. Four of these relations are still granted in symbolic logic. The exception is superimplication, which symbolic logic regards as an *invalid* inference. The reason is that if non-existent entities are talked about, the inference gives them existential import. If, however, *existent* entities are involved, the problem does not arise. Aristotle has been both praised and condemned for this mistake. On the one hand, he has been cited as an eminently practical man, who was concerned with scientific data, and not with non-existent entities. On the other hand, he has been condemned for failing to realize the necessary rigor of a deductive system. Since to err is human, it seems more appropriate neither to praise nor to condemn, but rather to recognize the error for what it is, and to forgive its author for not being omniscient.

Let us summarize, in tabular form, the immediate inferences of Aristotelian logic. The truth value of the premise is given in capital letters. When it has the truth value thus indicated, the corresponding statements (reading the table horizontally) will have the truth values indicated in lower case letters. The letter u is used to indicate that the statement is *undetermined* as to truth value (i.e., it may be either true or false), and does *not* indicate a third truth value.

A	E	I	O
T	f	t	f
f	T	f	t
u	f	T	u
f	u	u	T
F	u	u	t
u	F	t	u
f	t	F	t
t	f	t	F

Let us next take a brief look at some *mediate* inferences of the Aristotelian system. Here we shall make no attempt at completeness, for all the mediate inferences of Aristotelian logic can be handled easily by means of symbolic logic. Our purpose, rather, is merely to illustrate some of the ways in which mediate inferences are handled in the Aristotelian system. Consider the following argument:

> All humans are mortal.
> All mortals are ethical beings.
> Therefore all humans are ethical beings.

Arguments like this are known, in Aristotelian logic, as *"syllogisms"*. "Syllogism" has a somewhat different meaning for the classical logician than it does for the modern, symbolic logician. A syllogism, for the Aristotelian, is any argument containing two premises with two terms each, and a conclusion with two terms, and having also the characteristic that it contains three terms in all, each mentioned twice.

Certain arguments which meet these requirements are fallacious because there are several other requirements which also need to be met. (None of these, incidentally, need be remembered if *symbolic* logic is employed in proving validity.)

1. The most famous of these additional requirements is that the middle shall be distributed at least once. By the *"middle"* is meant the term that appears in both premises. A term is said to be distributed if, and only if, the statement in which it appears refers to all the individuals to which the term applies. Our sample syllogism is valid because the middle term, "mortal", is distributed in the second premise, where *all* mortals are referred to. This term is not, however, distributed in the first premise, since not all *mortals,* but only all *humans,* are referred to. It turns out that distributed terms are only those which are subject terms in universal statements (whether affirmative or negative), and predicate terms in negative statements (whether universal or existential). An argument like the following commits the *fallacy of undistributed middle:*

> All physicians have illegible handwriting.
> Some morons have illegible handwriting.
> Therefore some morons are physicians.

The symbolic statement of this argument readily reveals its invalidity:

$$(x)(P_x \supset I_x)$$
$$(\exists x)(M_x \cdot I_x)$$
$$\therefore (\exists x)(M_x \cdot P_x)$$

2. Another requirement of the valid Aristotelian syllogism is that a term cannot be distributed in the conclusion unless it is distributed in at least one of the premises. The following invalid argument illustrates a violation of this requirement:

> No fish are terrestrial creatures.
> Some things which swim are also terrestrial creatures.
> Therefore some fish don't swim.

Again, the invalidity of this argument is readily seen from its symbolic formulation:

$$(x)(F_x \supset \sim T_x)$$
$$(\exists x)(S_x \cdot T_x)$$
$$\therefore (\exists x)(F_x \cdot \sim S_x)$$

3. A third requirement of the valid Aristotelian syllogism is that it must have at least one affirmative premise. Nothing can be validly concluded if both premises are negative. An example of an argument which violates this requirement follows:

> No fish are terrestrial creatures.
> No terrestrial creatures make their usual habitat in the water.
> Hence no fish make their usual habitat in the water.

Or, symbolically:

$$(x)(F_x \supset \sim T_x)$$
$$(x)(T_x \supset \sim W_x)$$
$$\therefore (x)(F_x \supset \sim W_x)$$

4. And finally, the conclusion of the Aristotelian syllogism is negative if, and only if, one of its premises is negative. This is really a twofold requirement, specifying (case α) that if there is a negative premise, there must also be a negative conclusion; and that (case β) if there is a negative conclusion, there must be one negative premise. The following invalid arguments illustrate violations of this two-fold requirement:

Case α

> No fish are terrestrial creatures.
> All terrestrial creatures prefer land to water.
> Therefore all fish prefer land to water.

Or, symbolically:

> $(x)(F_x \supset \sim T_x)$
> $(x)(T_x \supset L_x)$
> $\therefore (x)(F_x \supset L_x)$

Case β

> All fish live in the water.
> All things which live in the water swim.
> Hence no fish swim.

Or, symbolically:

> $(x)(F_x \supset W_x)$
> $(x)(W_x \supset S_x)$
> $\therefore (x)(F_x \supset \sim S_x)$

Syllogisms are classified, in the Aristotelian system, according as the statements in them are A, E, I, or O statements. Thus a syllogism with two A premises and an A conclusion is an AAA syllogism. The AAA syllogism is regularly referred to as "the *Barbara* syllogism", because "Barbara" contains three A's. *Barbara* is a valid syllogism. Other valid syllogisms have different names, whereby to remember them. It should be evident that these devices are unnecessary if the arguments are treated in terms of symbolic logic, which easily handles them.

We have only scratched the surface of Aristotelian logic, by indicating somewhat the manner in which it operates. Let us hasten to stress that there is much more to the system than what has been covered in these few pages. At least we see, now, that Aristotelian logic is not a system wholly different from modern symbolic logic. It attempts to define the "rules of correct reasoning" as does symbolic logic, but in different terms. Symbolic logic covers the same territory that Aristotelian logic does, but it also covers much more than does the older system. A judgment to the effect that symbolic logic is *better than* Aristotelian logic cannot be made without considerable qualification. For the class of arguments encompassed by Aristotelian logic, the proper judgment is not so much one of "better than", but rather of "different from". Let us merely recognize the difference, and withhold any value judgment.

Index of Abbreviations

	Page			Page
A	208	B/D		136
A_1	15	Com		135
A_2	38	CP		153
A_3	46	D_I		78
A_4	50	D_{II}		81
A_5	50	D_{III}		86
A_6	59	D_{IV}		90
A_7	65	D_V		187
A_8	65	Dist		137
A_9	66	E		208
A_{10}	69	Exp		135
A_{11}	69	I		208
A_{12}	74	LE		137
A_{13}	173	O		208
A_{14}	177	Pr.		68
A_{15}	183	Q		193
A_{16}	185	S		140
Assump	152	Trans		133
Assump(IP)	158			

Index of Special Symbols

	Page		Page
⊃	15	(x)	164
∴	15	Φα	165
∠___	29	(α)	169
~	39	x*	173
∨	49	α*	173
·	63	(∃x)	180
=₍df₎	77	(∃α)	180
≡	85	c	210
Ⓥ	90	⊃ₛ	210

Index of Topics

Addition, principle of, 74
All-operator, 166
Alternation, principle of, 50
Analytic statement, 104
Antecedent, 25
Argument, 2–3
Aristotle, 1, 204, 207 ff.
Asterisk, 173
Atomic statement, 16, 53 ff.
Ayer, A. J., 203

Barbara, 214
Biconditional, 85
Braces, use of, 53 ff.
Brackets, use of, 53 ff.

Commutativity, 51, 135, 144–145
    of conjunction, 66
    of inclusive disjunction, 51
Conclusion, 3
Conjunct, 65
Conjunction, principle of, 63 ff.
Consequent, 25
Consistency, 119 ff., 194 ff.
Contingent statement, 105
Contradiction or contradictory statement, 105
Contradictoriness, 209–210
Contrariety, 210
Copi, Irving M., 204

Deduction or deductive logic, 5–6
Definition, 76 ff.

Definition I, 77 ff.
Definition II, 81
Definition III, 86
Definition IV, 90
Definition V, 187
Dilemma, constructive, 59 ff.
Disjunction, 49
    exclusive, 49, 89 ff.
    inclusive, 49, 89 ff.
Distribution, principle of, 136–137
Distribution of a term, 212
Dot, 63
Double negation, principle of, 69, 141 ff.

Elegance, 60
Equivalence, definitional, 77
    logical, 125 ff.
    of quantification, 188 ff.
Exportation, principle of, 134–135, 146

Fallacy, 36
    of affirming the consequent, 36
    of denying the antecedent, 44
    of undistributed middle, 212
Formal proof, 150
Frege, 207
Functional completeness, 76 ff., 162, 164–165, 169–170, 187 ff.

Generalization, existential, 182 ff.
    universal, 175 ff.

Horseshoe, 15
Hypothetical conditional, 24

Inconsistency, 119 ff.
Induction or inductive logic, 5–6
Inference, 4
  immediate, 208 ff.
  mediate, 209
Instance of an argument form, 16
Instantiation, existential, 182 ff.
  universal, 172 ff.
Invalidity, 11–13, 105

Logic, Aristotelian, 207 ff.
  classical, 207
  definition of, 1

Middle, 212
Mill, John Stuart, 204
Modus ponens, 15 ff.
Modus tollens, 38 ff.
Molecular statement, 16, 53 ff.

Necessary condition, 23 ff.
Negation, 39

Operator, logical, 76

Parentheses, use of, 53 ff.
Premise or premise set, 3
Proving validity, 28 ff.
  abbreviated method of, 67 ff.
  backward method of, 30
  by construction of formal proof,
    150
  conditional method of, 149 ff.,
    198 ff.
  indirect method of, 150, 156 ff.,
    198 ff.
  reductio ad absurdum method of, 110
    ff., 150, 194 ff.

Proving validity (*Continued*)
  truth table method of, 102 ff., 194
    ff.

Quantification, 162 ff.
  existential, 179 ff.
  particular, 180
  universal, 166 ff.
Quantifier, existential, 180
  universal, 166

Reductio ad absurdum, 110 ff., 158
Rhetoric, 1
Rosser, J. B., 204
Russell, 2, 204, 207

Schröder, 207
Scope, 168
Simplification, principle of, 64 ff.
Some-operator, 180
Soundness, 11–13
Square of opposition, 208–209
Statement variable, 15
Subcontrariety, 210
Subimplication, 210
Substitution, principle of, 140 ff.
Sufficient condition, 23 ff.
Superimplication, 210
Syllogism, 212
  Aristotelian, 212 ff.
  disjunctive, 50
  hypothetical, 46
Synthetic statement, 105

Tautology, 104
Tilde, 39
Transformation of biconditionals to
  exclusive disjunctions, and vice
  versa, 135–136
Transposition, principle of, 133–134,
  146

Triple bar, 85
Truth table, 93 ff.
  abbreviated, 100 ff.
  for any statement, 94
  for conjunction, 97
  for inclusive disjunction, 98–99
  for negation, 95
  for two statements, 96
  in Aristotelian logic, 211
  number of rows in, 109

Unsoundness, 12–13
Use and *mention,* 6, 15 n.

Validity, 11–13, 104
Variable, bound, 168
  free, 168

Wedge, 49
  circled, 89
Whitehead, A. N., 2, 204, 207